NGLISH
ESSENTIALS
With Self-Scoring Exercises

By Herbert B. Nelson

About the Author

1. Present postion: Professor of English and Head of English Department, Oregon State College.

2. Publications: Practice Leaves for Business English (Oregon State College, 1929); Teach Yourself Grammar (coauthor, Oregon State College, 1937); The Foundations of Good English (coauthor, Boston, Ginn and Company, 1938); The Foundations of Good English, Revised Edition, Form A (coauthor, Boston, Ginn and Company, 1951); The Foundations of Good English, Revised Edition, Form B (coauthor, Boston, Ginn and Company, 1952); The Literary Impulse in Pioneer Oregon (Oregon State Monograph, Studies in Literature and Language No. 1, 1948).

About the Book

1. A systematic review of essentials of English is provided.

2. Exercises are numerous enough to give ample review.

3. Scoring is easy.

4. Progress can be measured objectively from exercise to exercise.

5. Grammar exercises are simple, and the terms used are those of traditional grammar.

6. Three general review tests are given so that the user of the book may check his progress from time to time, or note his improvement as he goes through the exercises for the second or third time.

LITTLEFIELD COLLEGE OUTLINES
A. W. LITTLEFIELD, *General Editor*

* Asterisk indicates titles in the new Students Outline Series.

ENGLISH ESSENTIALS

With Self-Scoring Exercises

◆

By

HERBERT B. NELSON

Professor of English

Oregon State College

1958

LITTLEFIELD, ADAMS & CO.

Ames, Iowa

PREFACE

Probably everyone who holds this book in his hand has been exposed to *some* English grammar. He knows at least the names of the parts of speech, even if he is not always able to tell one from another. He usually knows when he has expressed a complete idea, and, most of the time, is able to decide correctly which number of a verb or which case of a pronoun should be used in his sentences. He has been writing and speaking the English language all his life, and usually he will decide correctly if he faces a choice of singular or plural verb, of nominative or objective case—even if these words mean little or nothing to him. However, he may have formed a bad habit, or he may be unable, at times, to make a correct decision on the basis of what he knows or remembers from his high school or elementary English class.

If your knowledge of English grammar is so hazy that the terms used in the paragraph above mean nothing to you, probably it would be wise, before you work the exercises, to turn to Part II of this book and begin a review of grammar. There you will *not* find a complete grammar, but you *will* find all the grammar you need to know to take you through an average freshman course in composition.

The purpose of this book will be to provide any student with enough basic practice material in English fundamentals to enable him to enter a regular freshman English class in any college or university. Most colleges screen their entering freshmen on the basis of some sort of placement test. Those students who are not successful in passing this test are placed in remedial sections. There they are given an opportunity to review the fundamentals before they enter a regular section. This book is designed to help these students.

Other students may pass the placement test but still make more errors in their compositions than instructors expect from college students. Generally, the instructor cannot take the time of the entire class to review elementary matters. The conscientious student first studies his handbook or rhetoric; then he works each exercise carefully. When it is completed to the best of his ability, he checks his answers with the answer sheet. If he misses any sentences, he may review his handbook or read the outlined rules and the sample sentences provided in this book. In a few days he may retest himself by covering the answers with a piece of paper and working the exercise again.

Three complete tests in fundamentals are also provided. A student may take one of these as he begins work, and after he has determined his score, may see in what decile or percentile he would place if he were an average entering freshman selected for college only because he had graduated from high school. The other tests may be used to measure progress and accomplishment.*

Every course in composition or communication stresses writing, and this writing should always be clear, effective, and accurate. I should like to point out to you that if your writing is not accurate, its other virtues are likely to be overlooked, and you will be stamped as one who tried to write but failed. Almost every failing grade given in the basic college course in composition is given because the student does not write accurately enough to satisfy minimum college standards.

For the student who wants to learn and who is not passively waiting to be taught, this book has been written. It does not pretend to be complete; it stresses only certain fundamental subjects because these are the ones that cause freshmen most trouble. It is not a substitute for a handbook of English or for a rhetoric; it is only a brief practice book of exercises in English. Used conscientiously it will assure you of at least a passing mark in your composition course.

---

* The following deciles are approximately those of average entering college freshmen.

Number of errors	Decile	Number of errors	Decile
0-35	10	53-56	5
36-42	9	57-59	4
43-46	8	60-62	3
47-50	7	63-70	2
51-52	6	71-?	1

TABLE OF CONTENTS

Part One

Part Two

ENGLISH ESSENTIALS

With Self-Scoring Exercises

PART I

Sentence Completeness

Probably the most serious error the careless or ignorant writer makes is failure to distinguish between what is a sentence and what is not. He will sometimes write a phrase or dependent clause as a complete sentence. Sometimes, too, he will run two sentences together without supplying the proper punctuation.

In English there are a great many sentence patterns. Some of them are short, some long, some extremely involved in their structure. To avoid too many short subject-first sentences, to avoid excessive use of compound sentences, students are frequently encouraged to learn new sentence patterns. They sometimes hesitate to try some of these, however, because they fear they may make serious errors if they experiment. Here are some complete sentences. Read them aloud to see what they sound like.

1. Mr. Jensen listened, holding his hat in his hands.
2. Like us, the farmer had come over two miles of drained marsh, but not by the route we had taken.
3. Until vacant spaces were settled, the scattered frontier farmers found themselves without schools, means of communication, or markets.
4. José de San Martín kept the revolutionary flame alive in a remote and recently settled province of La Plata.
5. In January, 1816, he began his epic march across the Andes with thirty-five hundred men, several thousand animals, and artillery, by a pass over half again as high as the Grand St. Bernard.
6. What as a boy he dreamed of doing, that he did.
7. Twenty-four, round faced, and on the plump side, he

is pictured as grasping a rifle and staring belligerently ahead.

8. The manager received us with smiling calm although he had suffered much that might have caused a slight bitterness.

9. Be so good as to listen to me.

10. They found her lying among the parcels spilled from her shopping bag, dead of heart failure.

11. Then we came to the McDonald Freeway.

12. Now her son-in-law and daughter were living with her, and glad they were to have a roof over their heads, for they had lost their home while he was serving in the navy during the war.

13. Although the Treaty of Ghent was a peace without a victory and the Americans did not attain a single objective for which their government had declared war, the people came to believe that they had won a just and glorious contest for free trade and seaman's rights.

14. Good morning, madam.

15. What if we are attacked?

16. Is it true that radio commercials to be effective must irritate the listener?

Here are some incomplete "sentences." Read each one aloud to see that something is lacking in it that must be supplied before the sentence makes sense. Practice completing these fragments in several ways.

1. Pop Western, the sole resident of a farm near a small town called Philomath, and with his struggle against a group of crooked politicians who have permitted the farm to fall into disrepair.

2. And that she lived in a town called Falls City near Dallas.

3. Thus wrecking his little plot.

4. To set off the large, two-story brick house with its high-ceilinged attic, from one of whose windows the flag hung on Decoration Day, the Fourth of July, and the birthdays of Washington and Lincoln.

5. Explaining that he was working on a commission and that his earnings were very small, amounting to twenty or thirty dollars a week.

6. His tone, almost as much as his words, revealing his

profound seriousness, his sadness at the state of the world, and his tempered hopes.

7. Recorded on film so that it can be run off again and again before all people in public life who employ television as a means of getting their ideas across.

8. A smooth, oily type often found, I am told, in big cities.

9. With the idea of making a million dollars, which he had succeeded in doing by the time he was forty-five, on an initial outlay of seventy-five dollars, by organizing and running a string of candy stores.

10. Where ball point pens lay heaped in gleaming piles on the counters of two aisles running almost the entire length of the Broadway side.

11. Behind the iron hitching post and granite carriage block at the curb, the McKay lawn, constantly sprinkled in the dry weather.

12. After pleading guilty to twenty-two traffic offenses, such as double-parking, having no driver's license, speeding, and driving in such a manner as to violate the basic rule.

Here are some "sentences" that contain more than enough for one complete sentence. Such "sentences" are called "run-together sentences," "fused sentences," "comma faults," or "comma splices." They are usually confusing to the reader and an indication that the author is not thinking in sentence units. Each one of these should be broken into more than one sentence. This may be done either by inserting in the proper place a period and a capital letter or by inserting a semicolon. For practical purposes one may consider the period and the semicolon as interchangeable although the semicolon is commonly used where there is a closer connection of ideas than would be true if the period and capital letter were used.

1. He has assembled forty pages of notes for a project, article, or book he hasn't decided which it will be.

2. On the opposite bank the seawalls that kept the estuary from doing harm were dark grey trees rising above them were black and without depth.

3. The winter wheat and oats were sending up green

blades bright as paint the plowed fields were squares of dark loam black and rich.

4. The grocer was not the only one everybody Mrs. Wells met this morning remembered how she laughed and joked.

5. The water runs away after that there's only a foot or two of water even at high tide.

6. The British minister could afford to show the lady marked attention, which was not difficult, for she had as much wit as beauty, however the dinners he gave in her honor were declined by other ladies, and at balls she was so snubbed that she soon gave up attempting social recognition.

7. I did not care to question them about the time I suspect about three years had passed.

8. "You can't get away with that they'll find it out," said a man who saw me do the damage.

9. "You don't know Sherlock Holmes yet," he said, "perhaps you would not care for him as a constant companion."

10. It was very late in the afternoon, nevertheless we were determined to delay our departure no longer.

11. The busiest writer produces little more than a volume a year, not so much as his talk would amount to in a week, consequently through speech it is usually decided whether a man is to have command of his language or not.

12. He was often asked to give advice to writers, however he disliked having the personal and psychological factors in criticism.

Exercises for

1. SENTENCE COMPLETENESS

Directions: In the blank space before each of the following write:

1. if the group of words would not ordinarily be punctuated as a complete sentence (sentence fragment);
2. if the group of words is a single complete sentence;
3. if the group of words as it stands constitutes more than would be punctuated as one complete sentence (comma fault or run-together sentence).

_____ 1. Often to the embarrassment of a shy wife.

_____ 2. Either he avoids the place for weeks, or else he works there from morning to night.

_____ 3. Another of his uncles, Wade Harvey, with whom he was living.

_____ 4. Well, let him call in the medicine man, I thought, it would not be the first time.

_____ 5. That nobody else can put over a song with an equal comprehension of what the composer had in mind.

_____ 6. Above, the bank was guarded by an unbroken range of steep acclivities.

_____ 7. The boys in the fraternity, however, were violently opposed to the plan presented by the dean.

_____ 8. "Surely there is not a moment to be lost," I cried, "shall I go and order you a cab?"

_____ 9. Having run away from a northern Minnesota farmer, to whom he had been "bound out."

_____ 10. Never missing a Sunday morning service unless he was ill or out of town.

_____ 11. Mrs. Smith wanted to believe in her husband there were too many times when she couldn't.

_____ 12. "You appear to be astonished," he said, smiling at my expression of surprise.

_____ 13. A stirring account of James and Esther Wilson and their dream of turning Africa's lush jungle growth to human benefit.

5

Exercises for

2. SENTENCE COMPLETENESS

Directions: In the blank space before each of the following write:

1. if the group of words would not ordinarily be punctuated as a complete sentence (sentence fragment);
2. if the group of words is a single complete sentence;
3. if the group of words as it stands constitutes more than would be punctuated as one complete sentence (comma fault or run-together sentence).

_____ 1. His eyes were truculent and yellowish-green, they seemed to grow fiery and dim and fiery again by turns.

_____ 2. Anxious as were all her conjectures on this point, it was not, however, the one on which she dwelt most.

_____ 3. That he had come to a place of worship for the purpose of worship and that he did not intend to tolerate a political speech in church.

_____ 4. I knew a general whose daughter fell in love with his adjutant, a clever and amiable young officer.

_____ 5. An inflexible straight-ticket Democrat living in a straight Republican neighborhood.

_____ 6. I have likened Joubert to Coleridge, indeed the points of resemblance between the two men are numerous.

_____ 7. The cluck of their oars was the only sound of any distinctness upon the sea, and as they labored amid the thickening shades, the lamp lights grew larger, each appearing to send a flaming sword deep down through the waves before him until there arose among other dim shapes of the kind, the form of the vessel for which they were bound.

_____ 8. This man was without exception the most murderous-looking villain I have ever had the misfortune to meet, that was the deliberate opinion I came to before I formed a closer acquaintance with him.

_____ 9. The coming of old age annoyed her like the coming of flies in summer.

Exercises for

3. SENTENCE COMPLETENESS

Directions: In the blank space before each of the following write:

1. if the group of words would not ordinarily be punctuated as a complete sentence (sentence fragment);
2. if the group of words is a single complete sentence;
3. if the group of words as it stands constitutes more than would be punctuated as one complete sentence (comma fault or run-together sentence).

_____ 1. Really great quotations are not manufactured, they sum up and express great experiences.

_____ 2. Rid yourself of the anxieties and tensions that interfere with the fulfillment of your personality.

_____ 3. Mr. Kelly was a little shorter than his wife, and he had a round, friendly, and self-important face.

_____ 4. American purchasing habits, being what they are.

_____ 5. Arthur was a free-lance actor, something of a critical success, and a financial flop.

_____ 6. Famous in the annals of the family for having once lifted a horse.

_____ 7. Shutting out the clip-clop of carriage horses on the street and the lazy splash of the fountain sprinkler swinging in circles in some shady corner of the lawn.

_____ 8. There were five bedrooms, some of them with closets as large as bathrooms, and the place seemed to us to be designed for games of hide-and-seek.

_____ 9. Watching her when she was down with a cold or fever or confined to bed as the result of falling from a stepladder in her pantry and breaking a rib.

_____ 10. Unlike the present phones, which have red numbers and black letters on a white background.

_____ 11. Probably the most important single element of a camera is the lens, great care should be exercised in its selection.

_____ 12. Thus by one vote did the legislature grant the people the privilege of gathering in constitutional convention.

Exercises for

4. SENTENCE COMPLETENESS

Directions: In the blank space before each of the following write:

1. if the group of words would not ordinarily be punctuated as a complete sentence (sentence fragment);

2. if the group of words is a single complete sentence;

3. if the group of words as it stands constitutes more than would be punctuated as one complete sentence (comma fault or run-together sentence).

_____ 1. Having outlived her husband by five years.

_____ 2. Machiavelli thought otherwise, nevertheless he studied the matter very thoroughly.

_____ 3. Bunches of bananas hung from the ceiling, most of them green, a few of them turning yellow.

_____ 4. Peterson, a short, bespectacled, gregarious, globular man with a Chamber of Commerce-like buoyancy, a vast gift for persuasion, and a restless instinct for selling things.

_____ 5. Nezhdanov lighted a candle, the gray night-moths flew in from the garden in showers and went toward the light.

_____ 6. It is not enough, however, by clearness and right emphasis to maintain interest, as the play develops, the interest should if possible be increased.

_____ 7. Judge Spencer's character of mind is reflected in his bearing and his physical appearance, he is a spruce, schoolmasterish man with a direct manner, and even in a soft summer shirt he gives the impression of wearing a wing collar.

_____ 8. I came to the city from the smug, small town of Stonefield—an inbred, traditional sort of southern town that makes you homesick before you leave it.

_____ 9. Mrs. Andrews knew Mrs. Mosley very well, she was a great friend of her eldest sister.

_____ 10. This habit, that like certain books I neglected to read until I was old enough to value them, deepened my sense of values.

Exercises for

5. SENTENCE COMPLETENESS

Directions: In the blank space before each of the following write:
1. if the group of words would not ordinarily be punctuated as a complete sentence (sentence fragment);
2. if the groups of words is a single complete sentence;
3. if the group of words as it stands constitutes more than would be punctuated as one complete sentence (comma fault or run-together sentence).

_____ 1. One of them, however, soon dropped out of the conversation and, edging away from the others, stood a little apart, leaning against the wall on the side of the porch.

_____ 2. The work of Richard Cirencester is extremely valuable as an account of the topography of early Britain, it is also interesting as the work of the first English antiquarian.

_____ 3. A vivid novel of Jamaica in the days when the threat of Napoleon heightened the fevered gaiety of the island.

_____ 4. A large part of the population poured down from the distressed areas in the north of England and obtained work in the industries of the South.

_____ 5. For almost thirty years the author has been a Presbyterian minister—a most unusual one since she is a woman, a wife, and a mother.

_____ 6. The motion for the convention was made for the eighth time, a long debate followed.

_____ 7. Fitch, who is now sixty-three, has been in the theater since he was twelve, having started out as a callboy at the Haymarket over the protests of his mother, a former school teacher.

_____ 8. After trying his hand at everything from school teaching to boilermaking.

_____ 9. Combining the appeal of *Rebecca* with the color of *The King's General* and the excitement of *My Cousin Rachel*, Daphne du Maurier has written her finest historical novel in the story of glamorous and intriguing Mary Anne Clark.

Exercises for

6. SENTENCE COMPLETENESS

Directions: In the blank space before each of the following write:

1. if the group of words would not ordinarily be punctuated as a complete sentence (sentence fragment);

2. if the group of words is a single complete sentence;

3. if the group of words as it stands constitutes more than would be punctuated as one complete sentence (comma fault or run-together sentence).

_____ 1. Today in one of the windows there are large cardboard signs.

_____ 2. You might call me a Russian, I was born in Odessa.

_____ 3. A far more important factor at 1300 feet than at lower altitudes.

_____ 4. Joe took off his second shoe, then he arranged the two highly polished black shoes side by side under the edge of the bed.

_____ 5. During which I saw a young woman frightened by a mouse.

_____ 6. Except for the story, apparently a well-authenticated one, that it was Constantine's mother who directed the excavations that led to the discovery of the pieces of wood that are venerated as parts of the True Cross, little is known about Saint Helena.

_____ 7. One of the pockets of the coat had been torn off the other was torn but was held in place with safety pins.

_____ 8. A small dance troupe that made its first appearance here last fall is back in town.

_____ 9. Twelve French knights came riding foremost in surcoats of blue velvet with sleeves of yellow silk, their horses trapped in blue, with white crosses powdered on their hangings.

_____ 10. She was dressed in purple velvet furred with ermine, her hair escaping loose.

_____ 11. "It is indeed kind of you to come," he said, "I have had everything left untouched."

Exercises for

7. SENTENCE COMPLETENESS

Directions: In the blank space before each of the following write:

1. if the group of words would not ordinarily be punctuated as a complete sentence (sentence fragment);

2. if the group of words is a single complete sentence;

3. if the group of words as it stands constitutes more than would be punctuated as one complete sentence (comma fault or run-together sentence).

_____ 1. Jim had chosen a hard chair, perhaps to keep himself awake, and he had a terrible struggle with sleep.

_____ 2. "What the deuce is the solar system to me?" he interrupted impatiently, "you say that we go round the sun."

_____ 3. Elizabeth was to reign without a rival, the undisputed sovereign of the hour.

_____ 4. Hammersly leaned forward his eyes took on a faraway look.

_____ 5. He took out his watch, said, "Oh, who cares what time it is," and gaily tossed the watch through an open window.

_____ 6. Ready to contribute men, money, and materials to make sure that there would be no hitch in the performance.

_____ 7. She tried to make her voice sound casual, now she moved slowly to the door that opened on the patio.

_____ 8. Which was on a hilltop that looked across the broad Willamette Valley and the distant blue heights of the Cascades.

_____ 9. When I was a boy and was taken to the circus, it was always an amazing thing to me that there should be so many people in the street moving in a direction _away_ from the circus.

_____ 10. Glorious as the spectacle was, however, it passed unheeded.

_____ 11. But he had developed a stubborn resolution to build the kind of house he wanted.

Exercises for

8. SENTENCE COMPLETENESS

Directions: In the blank space before each of the following write:

1. if the group of words would not ordinarily be punctuated as a complete sentence (sentence fragment);

2. if the group of words is a single complete sentence;

3. if the group of words as it stands constitutes more than would be punctuated as one complete sentence (comma fault or run-together sentence).

_____ 1. The pale man with big eyes standing there by the well with his young wife by his side.

_____ 2. This was a wonderful experience, one long to be remembered.

_____ 3. Where my people have lived for nearly a century.

_____ 4. How could this have happened to him?

_____ 5. A cow called in a deep, musical bass, a calf answered from a little pen by the barn.

_____ 6. "Californians are a race of people," said O. Henry, "they are not merely inhabitants of a state."

_____ 7. It was an hour later when the tall figure of a man appeared in the doorway, dusty, perspiring, eager.

_____ 8. I think my front tooth is loose, I can wiggle it a little.

_____ 9. This plan enabling the sailors to keep the boat heading into the waves.

_____ 10. When this story was first printed, the author received two kinds of letters, one asking a question, the other making a statement.

_____ 11. Having given up all hope of a return on his investment, Gavin sold his shares to his brother, who held them for six years.

_____ 12. With the understanding that Newman would pay him when the job was finished.

_____ 13. The renter in whose hands she had left the farm had proved a villain.

_____ 14. A poor country boy, he had gone to London to wait on guests in his uncle's hotel.

Exercises for

9. SENTENCE COMPLETENESS

Directions: In the blank space before each of the following write:

1. if the group of words would not ordinarily be punctuated as a complete sentence (sentence fragment);
2. if the group of words is a single complete sentence;
3. if the group of words as it stands constitutes more than would be punctuated as one complete sentence (comma fault or run-together sentence).

_____ 1. With well paid jobs and rapid promotions for those who make good.

_____ 2. *The Royal Family* is gossipy without being scandalous, it is filled with sidelights and anecdotes that humanize the family.

_____ 3. Nor did the drab clothes of the men and women provide any contrast to the ruins of the city.

_____ 4. "I'll be an assistant professor in three years," Poole said, "that will mean an increase in salary."

_____ 5. The sky being bluish and the sun shining through a slight haze when we arrived in the city.

_____ 6. The country was all we could expect, there being lakes everywhere and meadows patched with black plowland.

_____ 7. The story of Grand Coulee Dam, and especially of the bitter March day in 1952 when the life of one of the world's greatest powerhouses was threatened with extinction.

_____ 8. The polar extremes of poverty, on the one hand, and too much physical well-being, on the other, Highet regards as stultifying factors, forms of government, too, seem to him to play an important part in the blighting or blossoming of "man's unconquerable mind."

_____ 9. James Arthur Flanigan, who once played right end for Michigan, and is now regarded as one of the most promising ends in professional football.

_____ 10. The old homestead would certainly have been sold, indeed a potential buyer had already been located.

Exercises for

10. SENTENCE COMPLETENESS

Directions: In the blank space before each of the following write:

1. if the group of words would not ordinarily be punctuated as a complete sentence (sentence fragment);
2. if the group of words is a single complete sentence;
3. if the group of words as it stands constitutes more than would be punctuated as one complete sentence (comma fault or run-together sentence).

_____ 1. Apart from their drama, which was their weakest type of writing.

_____ 2. The whole problem, on which he had wasted his time, even his life, looked like a delusion.

_____ 3. The girl had gone off with a company of carnival performers, occasionally tidings of her came to the village of her glittering feats on the tight rope.

_____ 4. These are mere trifles, however, and not worth serious attention.

_____ 5. "I shall be delighted," she said, "I haven't attended many dances since my recent illness."

_____ 6. Main Street was a black swamp from curb to curb, on residence streets the grass parking strips oozed gray water.

_____ 7. The four hundred young men of the tribe put their arms over each other's shoulders, swaying in time to the one drum that ran like a dull, glowing thread through the singing.

_____ 8. Telling you how he detests and despises the decrepit society that has driven him to defend himself.

_____ 9. What has lingered has been a spiritual echo from feudalism.

_____ 10. The sentimental bandit is not robbing and murdering for his own benefit, he is doing it for the greatness of his country or for the emancipation of the poor.

Agreement of Subject and Verb

I. A verb agrees with its subject in number and person.

	Singular	_Plural_
1st person	I run	We run
2nd person	You run	You run
3rd person	He, she, it runs	They run

II. When words such as _included with, together with, in addition to, as well as,_ and _no less than_ intervene between the subject and the verb, the verb must still agree with the subject.

1. The _pilot,_ as well as his wife and children, _was_ shocked at the news.
2. The _teacher,_ not his pupils, _was_ absent.
3. _Mary,_ with June and Jane, _is_ attending the concert.
4. A _schedule_ for the dance, as well as a list of committees, _is_ printed on page one.
5. _Environment,_ no less than heredity, _forms_ the individual's character.

III. A singular subject requires a singular verb even though intervening words may be plural.

1. A _study_ of his latest paintings _shows_ remarkable improvement.
2. A _list_ of many books _has_ been given for suggested reading.
3. The _value_ of two methods in dealing with maladjustments—interviews and tests—_is_ great.
4. A new _order_ of ideas and principles _has_ been started.
5. This _book,_ containing both an index and a table of contents, _gives_ valuable information.

IV. The verb agrees with the subject, not with the predicate noun.

1. The best _time_ to see the stars _is_ the two hours after midnight.

15

2. The best *part* of this book *is* the introductory paragraphs.
3. The *material* of this desk *is* oak and steel.
4. *You,* the leader, *are* the man chosen to demonstrate the new weapon.

V. A compound subject connected by *and* takes a plural verb.

1. *Precision and speed* in typing *are* acquired by practice.
2. Her *beauty and poise make* her a desirable May queen.
3. Another *girl and I were* told to erase the board.

Exception: When the compound subject consists of two words of closely related meaning or of two nouns naming the same person, the verb is singular.

1. The best *singer and* best *scholar* here *is* Mary.
2. My *teacher and helper gives* me confidence.

VI. Use singular verbs with singular pronouns, including *each, either, anyone, neither, someone, anybody, everybody, nobody, one, no one.*

1. *Neither* of the girls *has* subscribed to this magazine.
2. *Everybody* in the room *was* silent.
3. *Every* dog and cat *is* to be given a license.
4. *Each* of the five patients *has* been cured.
5. *Someone* in there *is* making noise.
6. *Nobody* in the class *knows* the answer.

VII. *"None"* usually takes a plural verb unless a singular idea is clearly expressed.

1. *None* of them *are* willing to take the responsibility.
2. *None* of the members *has* a better right to speak.

VIII. When a subject is connected by *either - or,* or *neither - nor,* the verb is usually made to agree with the nearer.

1. Neither the *bus* nor its *occupants were* shaken.
2. Neither *Mary* nor the *Joneses sing* well.
3. Neither the *crew* nor the *captain was* saved.
4. Either *you* or your *brothers are* guilty of this crime.
5. Neither *you* nor *I am* likely to pass this way again.

IX. Use a singular verb when the subject is the name of a book, a poem, a newspaper, a motion picture, a drama, or the like.

1. *The Complete Works of Shakespeare is* an immense book.
2. *The New York Times is* an excellent paper.
3. *The Sad Sisters was* a strange movie.

X. Quantities and sums or multiples of numbers when expressing a single idea may take a singular verb.

1. *Thirty-six inches is* one yard.
2. *Seven and nine makes* sixteen.
3. *Four times six is* twenty-four.
4. *Two dollars is* too much to pay for those flowers.

XI. Fractions take a singular verb if the object of the following *of-phrase* is singular; they take a plural verb if the object of the following *of-phrase* is plural.

1. One-half of the *table has* been set.
2. One-quarter of the *pupils are* absent.
3. Two-thirds of the *cake has* been eaten.

XII. A relative pronoun referring to a singular antecedent should be followed by a singular verb; if it refers to a plural antecedent it should be followed by a plural verb.

1. Of the *movies that have* been imported from England this one is certainly the most fascinating.
2. I have just bought one of the new word *games which have* been sweeping the country.
3. Each of *us who are* now living will see many changes.
4. The *person who takes* time can do it.

XIII. "*There is*" should be followed by a singular noun; "*there are*" by a plural noun or nouns.

1. *There is* a *mouse* in the corner.
2. *There are* three *guests* coming this evening.
3. *There are* too many *children* in this school.
4. In the corner *there are* a *table* and *lamp* (a compound subject takes a plural verb).

XIV. Nouns plural in form but singular in meaning usually govern a singular verb.

1. *Economics* is a required subject.
2. The *mumps is* no longer a dread disease.
3. The *whereabouts* of Marie *is* unknown.

XV.　A collective noun requires a singular verb when the group is regarded as a unit, a plural verb when the action involves the members of the group.

1. The *jury is* selected.
2. The *jury are* unable to agree.
3. The *army is* camped nearby.
4. The *herd* of sheep *is* gone.

A list of collective nouns might include:

army	contents	group	offspring
audience	couple	herd	public
band	crowd	jury	remainder
class	dozen	mankind	rest
committee	flock	majority	row (of trees)
company	gang	number	team

XVI.　A *number* is plural; *the number* is singular.

1. *A number* of seamen *were* rescued by the destroyer.
2. *The number* of men lost *was* astonishingly low.

Exercises for

1. AGREEMENT OF SUBJECT AND VERB

Directions: In the blank space before each sentence write the number that stands for the correct verb form.

_____ 1. The janitor, together with four men from the physical plant, (1 has 2 have) been busy moving the furniture.

_____ 2. The present whereabouts of the addict (1 is 2 are) not known.

_____ 3. The great province of Bengal, together with Orissa and Bihar (1 has 2 have) long been governed by a viceroy.

_____ 4. There is a prize given for every man and woman who (1 appear 2 appears) in person at the Superette Market.

_____ 5. Neither the professor nor the graduate assistants (1 was 2 were) able to solve the problem.

_____ 6. In one corner of the gymnasium (1 hang 2 hangs) a punching bag.

_____ 7. One hundred dollars an acre (1 is 2 are) too much to pay for this farm.

_____ 8. There (1 was 2 were) a pile of books on his desk.

_____ 9. Both of the horses (1 has 2 have) been scratched from this race.

_____ 10. The growth of the children who lived in the slum districts (1 was 2 were) carefully checked by the health authorities.

_____ 11. Neither the salary nor the working hours (1 is 2 are) satisfactory.

_____ 12. She is one of those housemothers who (1 make 2 makes) everyone feel at home.

_____ 13. A number of residents on Grant Street (1 has 2 have) asked for street improvements.

_____ 14. The quality and size of the melons offered for sale (1 has 2 have) certainly deteriorated.

_____ 15. The subject of these lectures (1 has 2 have) been announced by the lecture committee.

_____ 16. I think that this is one of the best cakes that my wife (1 has 2 have) ever baked.

_____ 17. The bulldozers, trucks, and other heavy equipment (1 stand 2 stands) rusting in the yard.

Exercises for

2. AGREEMENT OF SUBJECT AND VERB

Directions: In the blank space before each sentence write the number that stands for the correct verb form.

_____ 1. He is the only one of the squad who (1 have 2 has) had previous experience.

_____ 2. Three-quarters of the amount (1 is 2 are) due now.

_____ 3. (1 Is 2 Are) there any lemons left in the refrigerator?

_____ 4. Two weeks (1 is 2 are) too short a time for the trip.

_____ 5. The proofs of his guilt (1 was 2 were) evident.

_____ 6. Nothing of their intentions (1 is 2 are) known.

_____ 7. The number of such misdemeanors (1 is 2 are) constantly increasing.

_____ 8. Many kinds of people (1 help 2 helps) in the work.

_____ 9. One of his greatest assets (1 is 2 are) his good humor.

_____ 10. The best plans of the ambassador (1 was 2 were) often thwarted.

_____ 11. There (1 are 2 is) several points to take into consideration.

_____ 12. Fifteen miles (1 is 2 are) much too far for an old man to walk.

_____ 13. It was one of the most successful stories that (1 has 2 have) been televised.

_____ 14. Either the children or their teacher (1 share 2 shares) the responsibility.

_____ 15. There (1 was 2 were) no bitterness in what he had to say.

_____ 16. Mrs. Jones is one of those women who (1 worries 2 worry) about trivialities.

_____ 17. The number of mistakes you have made (1 is 2 are) astonishing.

_____ 18. How many dollars (1 has 2 have) he paid you?

_____ 19. The house with its furnishings (1 was 2 were) sold at an auction.

Exercises for

3. AGREEMENT OF SUBJECT AND VERB

Directions: In the blank space before each sentence write the number that stands for the correct verb form.

_____ 1. *The Canterbury Tales* (1 is   2 are) by Geoffrey Chaucer.

_____ 2. Every one of us (1 have   2 has) some responsibility in the matter.

_____ 3. There (1 have   2 has) seldom been more confusion in our policy.

_____ 4. *Sonnets from the Portuguese* (1 is   2 are) by Elizabeth Browning.

_____ 5. A company of guardsmen (1 was   2 were) posted at the gate.

_____ 6. The doctor and his nurse (1 shares   2 share) the long night watches.

_____ 7. Neither my aunt nor my cousins (1 has   2 have) visited us for years.

_____ 8. Neither Williams nor I (1 have   2 has) received the contract.

_____ 9. The books he has, plus the book you gave him, (1 is   2 are) certainly enough.

_____ 10. The first of his many stories (1 seems   2 seem) true.

_____ 11. Neither of us (1 have   2 has) time for such foolishness.

_____ 12. Two dollars' worth of bananas (1 is   2 are) enough.

_____ 13. Steak with mushrooms (1 has   2 have) my vote every time.

_____ 14. The constant whir of the giant fans (1 bother   2 bothers) me.

_____ 15. Two-thirds of nine (1 is   2 are) six.

_____ 16. Neither my mother nor my two sisters (1 is   2 are) able to find my shoe.

_____ 17. Dealing with destruction and crimes of violence (1 is   2 are) his occupation.

_____ 18. His stillness and concentration (1 were   2 was) strangely impressive.

Exercises for

4. AGREEMENT OF SUBJECT AND VERB

Directions: In the blank space before each sentence write the number that stands for the correct verb form.

_____ 1. Neither of us (1 has   2 have) ever been to Mesa Verde.

_____ 2. Neither you nor your friends (1 is   2 are) aware of the serious situation.

_____ 3. He is clearly one of the greatest authorities that (1 have   2 has) ever written on the subject.

_____ 4. There (1 is   2 are) a number of considerations to be discussed.

_____ 5. Sixty-five cents of the amount collected (1 was   2 were) in nickels.

_____ 6. Doc is one of the few men I know who (1 grow   2 grows) begonias from seed.

_____ 7. Peggy or her two sisters (1 have   2 has) never seen the old home.

_____ 8. Neither Mr. Jones nor I (1 am   2 is   3 are) certain that you can do the work.

_____ 9. The secretary and her assistant (1 was   2 were) both busy.

_____ 10. In this block there (1 is   2 are) already two groceries.

_____ 11. Mary's only interest (1 is   2 are) in her home economics courses.

_____ 12. Not only the captain but the three mates (1 have   2 has) been vaccinated.

_____ 13. Monday, as well as Thursday, (1 was   2 were) reserved for ladies.

_____ 14. Neither Martin nor his two sons (1 have   2 has) a fishing license.

_____ 15. Robert is the only one of my children who (1 like   2 likes) to read.

_____ 16. A number of accidents (1 is   2 are) caused by the traffic dividers.

_____ 17. The number of cars on the road (1 is   2 are) increasing every year.

_____ 18. Both of the young men (1 was   2 were) to blame.

Exercises for

5. AGREEMENT OF SUBJECT AND VERB

Directions: In the blank space before each sentence write the number that stands for the correct verb form.

_____ 1. Neither you nor I (1 is 2 are 3 am) exempt from these taxes.

_____ 2. No home and no friends (1 awaits 2 await) me.

_____ 3. Neither the twins nor Mary (1 were 2 was) going to Seattle.

_____ 4. There (1 go 2 goes) my chances for an A!

_____ 5. There (1 is 2 are) nothing to be said for it.

_____ 6. Seven members of the party, including Andrews, (1 was 2 were) marooned.

_____ 7. (1 Do 2 Does) the author and publisher share alike in the profits?

_____ 8. Either you or she (1 is 2 are) to be the candidate.

_____ 9. Neither the elephant nor its trainer (1 was 2 were) there.

_____ 10. In the window the dust and cobwebs (1 was 2 were) thick.

_____ 11. A number of pages of his notes (1 was 2 were) lost.

_____ 12. *The Fifth Hour* is one of five plays of his that (1 has 2 have) been produced on Broadway.

_____ 13. This play is the only one of his that (1 has 2 have) made any money.

_____ 14. Either your experience or your textbooks (1 is 2 are) confusing you.

_____ 15. Everyone in the group (1 were 2 was) clothed in white.

_____ 16. The cards he held plus those I gave him (1 makes 2 make) him have fourteen.

_____ 17. To the victor (1 belong 2 belongs) the spoils.

_____ 18. The worst part of the program (1 was 2 were) the tenor solos.

_____ 19. A large supply of logs (1 was 2 were) taken aboard.

_____ 20. Children, accompanied by parents, (1 is 2 are) admitted free.

6. AGREEMENT OF SUBJECT AND VERB

Directions: In the blank space before each sentence write the number that stands for the correct verb form.

_____ 1. Portraits, together with an occasional landscape, (1 was 2 were) his stock in trade.

_____ 2. Either you or your brothers (1 is 2 are) liable for damages.

_____ 3. His is one of the most effective committees that (1 have 2 has) been appointed.

_____ 4. Both the inventor and his assistants (1 was 2 were) granted fellowships.

_____ 5. Ten pounds of coffee (1 is 2 are) enough for the whole group.

_____ 6. This volume is one of the many that (1 have 2 has) come from his press.

_____ 7. On the plate (1 was 2 were) a number of sardines on crackers.

_____ 8. This boa is one of the largest that (1 has 2 have) been brought back from the Amazon.

_____ 9. The most interesting part of the machine (1 is 2 are) the giant jaws.

_____ 10. Four per cent of the profits (1 was 2 were) paid back in taxes.

_____ 11. Neither of the boys (1 is 2 are) covered by insurance.

_____ 12. Both the employees and the business manager (1 appear 2 appears) to resent such practices.

_____ 13. There (1 is 2 are) no excuses for such actions!

_____ 14. The *Masterpieces of English Literature,* with its companion volumes, (1 was 2 were) returned to the shelf.

_____ 15. Ten cents' worth of candy (1 is 2 are) all Johnnie wants.

_____ 16. The committee (1 adhere 2 adheres) to its decision to limit the evidence.

_____ 17. Neither the janitor nor the secretary (1 has 2 have) made coffee.

_____ 18. Ten cans of coffee (1 cost 2 costs) twelve dollars.

_____ 19. Four-fifths of the money (1 was 2 were) in silver.

Agreement of Pronoun and Antecedent

I. A pronoun agrees with its antecedent in number, person, and gender.

    1. The following *people* failed the composition course for which *they* were registered.

    2. The *boy*, accompanied by his four classmates, took *his* dog with *him*.

    3. The sawmill *workers* said that *they* needed a wage increase.

II. A singular pronoun is used with *each, every, either, neither, someone, somebody, anyone, anybody, everyone, everybody, no one, nobody,* etc. or with a series of words introduced by one of them.

    1. When the test began, *each* student placed *his* books on the floor.

    2. If *anybody* heard this tale, *he* would doubt my sanity.

    3. *Every* girl will be asked to donate some of *her* time to working on the committee.

    4. *Every* man, woman, and child is being called upon to do *his* duty.

    5. *Neither* Williams nor Andrews is playing *his* best game.

III. When the antecedent includes persons of both sexes, a singular masculine pronoun is used.

    1. *Every student* must have *his* own textbook.

    2. *Each boy and girl* in the class must hand in *his* lesson now.

IV. With collective nouns use either a singular or plural pronoun according to the meaning of the sentence.

    1. The *class* nominated *its* officers by secret ballot.

    2. The *class* took *their* seats promptly.

V.   If two or more antecedents are connected by *and*, a plural pronoun is used.

1.   *His children and mine* started on *their* way to kindergarten.
2.   The *Indian guide and I* had lost *our* way.
3.   *Jean and Walter* do *their* best to make the play a triumph.

VI.   When a pronoun refers to a singular and a plural antecedent, it should agree with the nearer antecedent.

1.   Either *Louis* or his *friends* may miss *their* train.
2.   Neither *May* nor her *classmates* will wear *their* hats.

VII.   Indefinite pronouns should be consistent.

1.   When *you* have worked there a day, *you* will be tired.
     (Not: When *one* has worked there a day, *you* will be tired.)
2.   When *one* has worked here a day, *he* will be tired.
3.   After *you* have seen this picture, *you* will be happy.

VIII.   A pronoun should not be used instead of a noun if there may be doubt about its antecedent.

1.   John told his father that he (John) would win.
     (Not: John told his father that he would win.)
2.   We took out the oranges and threw the boxes away.
     (Not: We took the oranges out of the boxes and threw them away.)

IX.   Avoid the use of *this, that, which, it* to refer to the whole idea of a preceding clause instead of to a specific noun in the clause.

1.   Do not write on both sides of the paper. *This* is not really economical.
2.   He was always friendly and good-humored, *which* made everybody like him.

X.   Avoid the use of *it, you, they*, to refer to an indefinite antecedent.

1.   My father spent his early life on a farm. It influenced his whole life.
2.   I always like to visit New Orleans; they have such a colorful Mardi Gras.

Exercises for

1. AGREEMENT OF PRONOUN
AND ANTECEDENT

Directions: In the blank space before each sentence mark an X if there is an error in the agreement of pronoun and antecedent.

_____ 1. A person must at all times guard themselves against slanderous tongues.

_____ 2. Someone has been here and left her calling card.

_____ 3. The sonnet was introduced by Wyatt and Surrey. They were love poems of fourteen lines.

_____ 4. Needless to say, everyone who invested in that stock lost their money.

_____ 5. If one becomes discouraged, you lose interest.

_____ 6. Everyone of the veterans was responsible for their own lodging.

_____ 7. When anyone is irritated, it is best to let him alone.

_____ 8. Every pilot returned safely from their dangerous mission.

_____ 9. Everyone was dressed in his best and glad to be at the party.

_____ 10. Bernie told his partner that he was a failure.

_____ 11. They were told that all of the men would have to wait their turn.

_____ 12. Each of the dogs entered in this race has won his share of trophies.

_____ 13. We enjoyed our visit to the Bar X Ranch very much. They were extremely hospitable people.

_____ 14. The one or two members of the class who raise their hands answer most of the questions.

_____ 15. Either my sister or her roommate may miss her bus.

_____ 16. Neither of the two secretaries had brought their lunch.

_____ 17. Each of the horses entered their stall.

_____ 18. Neither of the boys would admit that he had missed school.

_____ 19. Every actor and actress in Hollywood expected that they would be invited to attend the wedding.

Exercises for

2. AGREEMENT OF PRONOUN AND ANTECEDENT

Directions: In the blank space before each sentence mark an X if there is an error in the agreement of pronoun and antecedent.

_____ 1. Both of the stone masons had done their work very well.

_____ 2. Has everyone here sent their mother a gift for Mother's Day?

_____ 3. People certainly have no right to shout "Fire!" if they are in a crowded theater.

_____ 4. No one has any idea what his quota will be.

_____ 5. Oregon State College prides itself on giving each student their own diploma.

_____ 6. Either Bannister or Landy is able to break the four-minute mile again if they have a good day.

_____ 7. Neither of the girls was convinced that she had baked a prize-winning cake.

_____ 8. There is always someone at every party who feels that they should try on the ladies' hats.

_____ 9. If anyone goes fishing in that area, they may expect to catch fish.

_____ 10. Either of you may go if he gets permission from the monitor.

_____ 11. Each person should hold his ticket in his hand.

_____ 12. I am not one of those people who believe that they can get something for nothing.

_____ 13. I would not ask every teacher to give me so much of her valuable time.

_____ 14. Brophie is one of those men who think they can do no wrong.

_____ 15. Neither the farmer nor his three sons have ever sold any of their land.

_____ 16. Several of the investors in that vicinity lost all their money.

_____ 17. Almost everyone has some keepsake that he cherishes.

_____ 18. The members of the band are trying out their new instruments.

Exercises for

3. AGREEMENT OF PRONOUN AND ANTECEDENT

Directions: In the blank space before each sentence mark an X if there is an error in the agreement of pronoun and antecedent.

_____ 1. Each student is required to do his own research.

_____ 2. At this point everyone in the audience expressed their approval by applauding.

_____ 3. Mr. Ross told Mrs. Ross that she could visit an antique shop, which made her very happy.

_____ 4. None of us at the club could learn what he should do about lowering his handicap.

_____ 5. One's friends often hinder your progress.

_____ 6. One frequently finds that his mistakes come back to haunt him.

_____ 7. Everyone here denies that the responsibility is theirs.

_____ 8. It was clear that everyone at the picnic had taken as much as his plate would hold.

_____ 9. Some of the residents did their best to block the amendment.

_____ 10. Every person who has such varied duties must do their best to budget their time.

_____ 11. Ask anyone what he thinks of this arrangement, and he will tell you that it is the best possible under the circumstances.

_____ 12. If a person wishes to see a western cattle town, he should visit Burns, Oregon.

_____ 13. I wonder why no one has considered abandoning his home in the flooded area.

_____ 14. We always admire someone who, when conditions are difficult, still does their best.

_____ 15. If everybody knew how cool the summers are in Oregon, they would spend their vacation there.

_____ 16. Neither child could be taught to write legibly with his right hand.

_____ 17. Whoever used this machine last certainly did his work in a careless manner.

Exercises for

4. AGREEMENT OF PRONOUN AND ANTECEDENT

Directions: In the blank space before each sentence mark an X if there is an error in the agreement of pronoun and antecedent.

_____ 1. From newspaper accounts I learned of your being selected to head that department.

_____ 2. If any man, woman, or child wishes to change their mind, this is the time to do it.

_____ 3. Few people were able to judge their speed accurately at the intersection.

_____ 4. Both painters are masters of their art.

_____ 5. If anyone refuses to go, let him remain at home.

_____ 6. Everyone who attended the council meeting expressed their dissatisfaction with the paving project.

_____ 7. If someone comes in, tell them I shall be back after lunch.

_____ 8. If the new manager arrives during the day, he should visit the store.

_____ 9. When one has worked as hard as I, you will want more recognition.

_____ 10. All the girls came to the bus with their suitcases and sleeping bags.

_____ 11. We visited Yosemite National Park, which was a thing we had always wanted to do.

_____ 12. We visited England in the summer of 1954. They had just gone off meat rationing.

_____ 13. Everyone will take his own helmet as he enters the gate.

_____ 14. If any student should injure himself in the laboratory, is the instructor liable?

_____ 15. Every representative of the company must show their pass before they can be admitted.

_____ 16. No one would wish to have this happen to them.

_____ 17. The speaker enjoyed the coffee hour at the Memorial Union. They were very friendly and courteous.

CASE OF PRONOUNS

Personal Pronouns

Singular

Nominative	Possessive	Objective
1st person I	my, mine	me
2nd person you	your, yours	you
3rd person he, she, it	his, her, hers, its	him, her, it

Plural

1st person we	our, ours	us
2nd person you	your, yours	you
3rd person they	their, theirs	them

Relative or Interrogative Pronouns

Singular and Plural

who	whose	whom
whoever	whosever	whomever
whosoever	whosesoever	whomsoever

I. Use the nominative case for the subject of a verb and after forms of the verb *be* (i.e., is, are, was, were, been).

1. *I* want to make this matter clear.
2. *You* are completely right, James.
3. *They* have little choice in making their decisions.
4. It is *he*.
5. It could certainly not have been *they*.

II. Use the objective case of a pronoun as the object of a verb, a verbal, or a preposition, and also as the indirect object of a verb.

1. *Whom* did she marry?
2. A group *of us* girls went to the beach.
3. This story is *between you* and *me*.
4. The Chamber of Commerce sent Mr. Moore and *me* some information.

III. Place an appositive in the same case as its antecedent.

31

    1. *We three—Mary, you* and *I*—are about to leave.
    2. He spoke to *us* three—*Alice, you* and *me.*
    3. Let's go skating, *him, Betty,* and *me.*

IV.   After the conjunctions *than* and *as* the pronoun is in nominative or objective case according to the meaning of the sentence.

    1. My roommate was younger than *I* (am young).
    2. I am not so handsome as *he* (is handsome).
    3. She saw him before *I* (saw him).
    4. Joe likes her better than (he likes) *me.*

V.   The possessive case is used to modify a gerund.

    1. *His* leaving the office early puzzled me.
    2. I could not understand *his* throwing a tantrum over such a slight matter.
    3. The bus has already gone; *its* leaving early has made me miss my dentist's appointment.

VI.   The pronoun used in a participial construction is in the objective case.

    1. I cannot picture *him* doing such a thing.
    2. I have seen *him* chasing the ball.

VII.   The subject of an infinitive is in the objective case.

    1. Joseph wanted *me* to give *him* a small gift. (*Me,* the subject of the infinitive *give,* and *him* the complement of *give* are both in the objective case.
    2. John thought *him* to be *me.* (*Me* is in the objective case, as is *him,* the subject of the infinitive.)
    3. I was introduced to the man *whom* we thought to be the general. (*Whom* is the subject of the infinitive *be.*)

Exercises for

1. CASE OF PRONOUNS

Directions: In the blank space before each sentence write the number that stands for the correct form of the pronoun.

_____ 1. No matter how you look at it, it was (1 she   2 her) whom they opposed.

_____ 2. My sister, who is two years older than (1 I   2 me), is much less hopeful.

_____ 3. Everybody stood erect except Dick and (1 I   2 me).

_____ 4. None was better prepared for the profession than (1 he   2 him).

_____ 5. Jack can play ball as well as you or (1 I   2 me).

_____ 6. We considered (1 she   2 her) to be the best actress in the company.

_____ 7. It must have been (1 he   2 him).

_____ 8. If I were (1 she   2 her), I would get a permanent.

_____ 9. None was more kind than (1 she   2 her).

_____ 10. You have lived here longer than (1 we   2 us).

_____ 11. It was (1 she   2 her) they considered last.

_____ 12. I must admit, between you and (1 I   2 me), I failed that last test.

_____ 13. The club sent three members to represent them— Tom, Don, and (1 I   2 me).

_____ 14. (1 Who   2 Whom) are they asking?

_____ 15. Nobody can be as lucky as (1 he   2 him).

_____ 16. Everybody had supposed it was (1 he   2 him) who threw the rock through the window.

_____ 17. For you and (1 she   2 her) to walk twenty-five miles would be tiring.

_____ 18. It is always (1 I   2 me) who gets severely punished.

_____ 19. Why were you counting on (1 they   2 them) to bring the cake?

_____ 20. Jack asked Mary rather than (1 I   2 me) to go to the show.

33

Exercises for

2. CASE OF PRONOUNS

Directions: In the blank space before each sentence write the number that stands for the correct form of the pronoun.

_____ 1. (1 Who 2 Whom) did it seem would be nominated?

_____ 2. The army sent three men to the conference—General Dans, General Bixby, and (1 I 2 me).

_____ 3. The campus policeman swore it was (1 they 2 them) that he had seen.

_____ 4. We were shown over the capitol by a man (1 who 2 whom) we understood to be the official guide.

_____ 5. He was the one (1 who 2 whom) the staff selected for the task.

_____ 6. I must admit, between you and (1 I 2 me), that you are right.

_____ 7. We could not determine (1 whom 2 who) he was supposed to represent.

_____ 8. I saw your husband and (1 he 2 him) at the ball game.

_____ 9. Mrs. Colby was pleased about (1 him 2 his) playing in the orchestra.

_____ 10. I could not understand (1 him 2 his) saying such a wicked thing.

_____ 11. That is a child (1 who 2 whom) should be disciplined.

_____ 12. Just the two of us, my sister and (1 I 2 me), were permitted to leave.

_____ 13. Is she the person (1 who 2 whom) you thought she was?

_____ 14. It is (1 he 2 him) who wants to read that book.

_____ 15. This is the man (1 who 2 whom) won the trophy.

_____ 16. Sell the bicycle to (1 whomever 2 whoever) makes the best offer.

_____ 17. The woman (1 who 2 whom) we just met is my neighbor.

_____ 18. He is the boy with (1 who 2 whom) I should like to go to the dance.

_____ 19. The club will accept (1 whoever 2 whomever) you choose.

Exercises for

3. CASE OF PRONOUNS

Directions: In the blank space before each sentence write the number that stands for the correct form of the pronoun.

_____ 1. I knew it was (1 she 2 her).

_____ 2. (1 Whoever 2 Whomever) applies will be granted a courteous interview.

_____ 3. Be sure to take a companion (1 who 2 whom) you can depend upon.

_____ 4. The witness identified the prisoner (1 who 2 whom) the officer had captured.

_____ 5. (1 Whoever 2 Whomever) they select will be sent to Chicago.

_____ 6. Several of (1 we 2 us) tennis players went to Seattle for the tournament.

_____ 7. If I were (1 her 2 she), I would wash it out with alcohol.

_____ 8. No one was a better hostess than (1 her 2 she).

_____ 9. Three of us—Homer, Baxter, and (1 me 2 I)—went for a long walk.

_____ 10. The widow was left with three children (1 who 2 whom) she was expected to support.

_____ 11. There is little reason for (1 him 2 his) staying any longer.

_____ 12. Certainly it could not have been (1 they 2 them).

_____ 13. Mrs. Root gave the information to (1 whoever 2 whomever) asked for it.

_____ 14. Their mother questioned (1 we 2 us) boys for several minutes.

_____ 15. (1 Who 2 Whom) could the visiting star have thought he was?

_____ 16. Let's you and (1 I 2 me) go home for lunch.

_____ 17. The young man (1 who 2 whom) you met yesterday is our new staff member.

_____ 18. It was (1 he 2 him) who was visiting my sister.

_____ 19. You have done this as often as (1 I 2 me).

_____ 20. Please give this package to (1 whoever 2 whomever) he sends.

Exercises for

4. CASE OF PRONOUNS

Directions: In the blank space before each sentence write the number that stands for the correct case of the pronoun.

_____ 1. My sister, who is four years younger than (1 I 2 me) just graduated from high school.

_____ 2. I would not like the enemy to be (1 they 2 them).

_____ 3. That student (1 who 2 whom) we thought was graduated last year is still in school.

_____ 4. I shall bring tickets for (1 whoever 2 whomever) is invited.

_____ 5. He was a man (1 who 2 whom), I think, has never known what it is to be hungry.

_____ 6. It is he, Jim, (1 who 2 whom) wants to read the book.

_____ 7. This matter does not concern either your parents or (1 we 2 us).

_____ 8. Betty gave tests to three of the students—Bascom, Eilers, and (1 I 2 me).

_____ 9. Possibly it was (1 her 2 she) whom you saw at the police station.

_____ 10. (1 Who 2 Whom) do you think the baby resembles?

_____ 11. I should never have suspected those culprits to be (1 them 2 they).

_____ 12. Nobody cared to know (1 who 2 whom) Mrs. Smythe had invited.

_____ 13. The company expects to send Baxter and (1 I 2 me) on a trip.

_____ 14. His wife manages the estate better than (1 he 2 him).

_____ 15. (1 Who 2 Whom) are the twelve delegates expected to elect the chairman?

_____ 16. The girl standing in the doorway might have been (1 her 2 she).

_____ 17. Everybody attended the concert except Molly and (1 her 2 she).

_____ 18. Mary is the one waitress (1 who 2 whom) they should pay a higher salary.

Exercises for

5. CASE OF PRONOUNS

Directions: In the blank space before each sentence write the number that stands for the correct case of the pronoun.

_____ 1. His manager is not as strong as (1 he 2 him).

_____ 2. I believe (1 she 2 her) to be capable of doing the work.

_____ 3. Please extend my greetings to (1 whoever 2 whomever) comes.

_____ 4. Everyone except you and (1 I 2 me) came early.

_____ 5. The man in the boat was (1 him 2 he).

_____ 6. (1 Who 2 Whom) do you think the president will appoint?

_____ 7. The man (1 who 2 whom) they think is guilty will be closely observed.

_____ 8. Do not blame William and (1 I 2 me).

_____ 9. The culprits, (1 he and I 2 him and me), were punished.

_____ 10. This matter must be settled between you and (1 he 2 him).

_____ 11. He took the blame for James and (1 me 2 I).

_____ 12. I knew it was (1 she 2 her) by her perfume.

_____ 13. (1 Who 2 Whom) do you think made the error?

_____ 14. (1 She 2 Her) and her husband worked hard for twenty years.

_____ 15. I thought it to be (1 him 2 he).

_____ 16. (1 Us 2 We) boys went skating on the pond.

_____ 17. The message meant little to either Andy or (1 me 2 I).

_____ 18. Ruth asked Jack and (1 me 2 I) to go with Jane and her.

_____ 19. Forgive my not knowing (1 whom 2 who) you are.

_____ 20. Never let anything come between you and (1 I 2 me).

Exercises for

6. CASE OF PRONOUNS

Directions: In the blank space before each sentence write the number that stands for the correct case of the pronoun.

_____ 1. (1 Whoever 2 Whomever) you select will be satisfactory to me.

_____ 2. The man in the dark coat was (1 he 2 him).

_____ 3. Name three men (1 who 2 whom) you believe to be qualified.

_____ 4. The Greek writing meant nothing to either of us—John or (1 I 2 me).

_____ 5. (1 Whom 2 Who) shall I thank for this fine gift?

_____ 6. Please think of Bert and (1 I 2 me) as your friends.

_____ 7. (1 Whom 2 Who) do you think is to blame?

_____ 8. There remains the possibility that it might have been (1 she 2 her).

_____ 9. The teacher gave three of us—Bill, John, and (1 I 2 me)—a severe look.

_____ 10. I asked everyone except Mary and (1 she 2 her) to the party.

_____ 11. I knew that (1 whoever 2 whomever) I chose would have his share of troubles.

_____ 12. Three of us—John, Bill, and (1 I 2 me)—were late to class.

_____ 13. I give my blessing to (1 whoever 2 whomever) succeeds me.

_____ 14. We shall give an orchid to (1 whomever 2 whoever) comes into the store early enough.

_____ 15. (1 Us 2 We) girls have fun on our sun porch.

_____ 16. Could it have been (1 I 2 me) whom she meant?

_____ 17. We organized the campaign around Ann and (1 her 2 she).

_____ 18. How could it have been (1 they 2 them) who were caught in the storm?

_____ 19. James and (1 him 2 he) were first in line.

_____ 20. If you can, I should like you to go with (1 she and I) (2 her and me).

PRINCIPAL PARTS OF IRREGULAR VERBS

Knowing the principal parts of verbs will enable you to use their correct forms, that is to conjugate them. The principal parts are the present, past, and past participle. You may supply the word *now* to see the use of the present, as in "I see it *now*," "He plays *now*," "They run *now*." The past tense is the form you would use with the word *yesterday*, as "I saw it *yesterday*," "He played *yesterday*," "They ran *yesterday*." The past participle is the form used with *have, has* or *had*, as "I *have* seen it," "He *has* played," "They *had* run."

Regular verbs form their past tense and past participles by adding *d* or *ed* to the present.

Present	Past	Past Participle
close	closed	closed
play	played	played

The principal parts of irregular verbs must be learned. Study the following list:

Present	Past	Past Participle
arise	arose	arisen
awake	awoke	awaked
become	became	become
begin	began	begun
bite	bit	bitten
break	broke	broken
burst	burst	burst
choose	chose	chosen
come	came	come
dive	dived	dived
do	did	done
drink	drank	drunk
drive	drove	driven
forget	forgot	forgotten
freeze	froze	frozen
get	got	got

Present	_Past_	_Past Participle_
go	went	gone
hang	hung, hanged (executed)	hung, hanged
lay	laid	laid
lie (recline)	lay	lain
raise	raised	raised
ride	rode	ridden
ring	rang	rung
rise	rose	risen
shake	shook	shaken
shine	shone	shone
show	showed	shown
shrink	shrank	shrunk, shrunken (adj.)
sit	sat	sat
sing	sang	sung
sink	sank	sunk
slay	slew	slain
speak	spoke	spoken
spring	sprang	sprung
swear	swore	sworn
swim	swam	swum
take	took	taken
wear	wore	worn
weave	wove	woven

Exercises for

1. VERB FORMS

Directions: In the blank space before each sentence mark an X if there is an error in the form of the verb.

____ 1. Poor Alice was so frightened that she shrunk away from him.

____ 2. The jeweler has shown me several beautiful pins.

____ 3. The old Indian squaw had wove her last basket.

____ 4. The sitter had sung little Andy to sleep at last.

____ 5. The rebels had laid a deep plot.

____ 6. The deer lifted her head after she had drank her fill.

____ 7. Sam Taylor, bandit extraordinary, had slew forty-seven men.

____ 8. She had obviously bitten off more than she could chew.

____ 9. When I come to the West, it was still possible to homestead land.

____ 10. The dusty volume has lain on the shelf for years.

____ 11. The wild horse, Montana, had been broke to the saddle.

____ 12. I almost froze my hands in the cold mountain stream.

____ 13. The swollen Rio Grande has burst its banks.

____ 14. He had awaked from a deep dream.

____ 15. My niece had began to notice the boys.

____ 16. He had lain his head upon her lap and sobbed bitterly.

____ 17. The wintry moon shone on her reclining figure.

____ 18. Old Shep come home yesterday and found that his master had moved.

____ 19. I must lay down now and rest my weary head.

____ 20. William Blalock has spoken his own epitaph.

____ 21. Four shots had rang out from the barn.

____ 22. You have chosen your bed; now you must lie on it.

____ 23. Have you ever swum across the river?

____ 24. They laid poor Jesse in his grave.

____ 25. I had shook hands with the rascal before I realized.

Exercises for
2. VERB FORMS

Directions: In the blank space before each sentence mark an X if there is an error in the form of the verb.

_____ 1. His imported shoes had finally wore out.

_____ 2. Dave laid his pipe on his desk.

_____ 3. Why are you sitting so still?

_____ 4. The barometer today had rose a little.

_____ 5. When the alarm clock rang, I had already awaked.

_____ 6. The girl had broke her arm when she fell from the tree.

_____ 7. You may lay down for a few minutes after lunch.

_____ 8. From this disagreement had sprung all their trouble.

_____ 9. Jack dove from the side of the tank.

_____ 10. The girl next door laid in the sun too long.

_____ 11. Sit this tray on the table by the bed.

_____ 12. The heavy rains had raised the level of the river two feet above flood stage.

_____ 13. When I became more efficient, I broke my old record.

_____ 14. He had somehow got his foot caught in the trap.

_____ 15. Have you ever in your life sang so well?

_____ 16. The Indian basket had been woven of willow.

_____ 17. In the depths of winter have you ever went skating along the river?

_____ 18. Little Tommy came running to his mother, crying that a snake had bitten him.

_____ 19. The dog has laid by the stove a long time.

_____ 20. Everyone admitted the strength and courage he had showed.

_____ 21. I heard him say that he done well on the examination.

_____ 22. The little girl laid in her bed for two days.

_____ 23. After murdering forty men, the bandit was hanged.

Exercises for
3. VERB FORMS

Directions: In the blank space before each sentence mark an X if there is an error in the form of the verb.

_____ 1. With proper training Peter could have become a great artist.

_____ 2. Yesterday, I run up to the ranch to see how the foreman was.

_____ 3. We have not forgot how much we owe to them.

_____ 4. The old coat had hung in the hall closet for months.

_____ 5. That evening I drunk the bitter dregs of defeat.

_____ 6. James lay his head on his arms and went to sleep.

_____ 7. McAndrew dived into the pool with reckless courage.

_____ 8. The inspector had spoke to him about it in April.

_____ 9. If you had not shaken me, I could never have arisen.

_____ 10. This morning the flag was raised at dawn.

_____ 11. The doctor told him that he should lay down for a few minutes after every meal.

_____ 12. The horse had obviously been ridden hard.

_____ 13. Slowly the animal sunk from sight in the quicksand.

_____ 14. The sun arose that morning at 6:05.

_____ 15. He done me a favor when he sold me old Paint.

_____ 16. I laid my hand on his head and patted it.

_____ 17. The gangster had swore he was in St. Louis.

_____ 18. With a shudder, she shrank from the sight.

_____ 19. He showed Hank how to string a bow.

_____ 20. It was dawn when Evelyn arose.

_____ 21. Murray lay in the dust, sobbing quietly.

_____ 22. "Come quickly," his wife said; "the water pipe has bursted."

_____ 23. The picture was hung in the art center.

_____ 24. I have never in my life drank such cold water.

_____ 25. She had obviously become bored with the conversation.

Exercises for

4. VERB FORMS

Directions: In the blank space before each sentence mark an X if there is an error in the form of the verb.

_____ 1. Peter had drove off in his truck before I arrived.

_____ 2. Seldom have more records been broken in one track meet.

_____ 3. We agreed that we should never have chose him as president.

_____ 4. The testimony clearly showed that the old man's hand had shaken very badly when he signed his will.

_____ 5. On Easter she had proudly wore her new white coat and blue hat.

_____ 6. I must lie down now; the doctor has ordered me to lie down after every meal.

_____ 7. The organ music began, and the congregation sang with great gusto.

_____ 8. The big cat had laid in his cage all day without moving a muscle.

_____ 9. The clerk has shone me nothing that I would buy.

_____ 10. The curtain will raise at eight o'clock sharp.

_____ 11. William laid his compass carefully in his box and began to sharpen his pencil.

_____ 12. The water main in front of his store had busted.

_____ 13. The intelligent animal had already began to gnaw the ropes.

_____ 14. The old revolver had lain in the drawer for many years.

_____ 15. Last year I became a member of the sheriff's posse.

_____ 16. The tiny kitten had become entangled in the yards of pink ribbon.

_____ 17. The porpoise very easily swam away from the small dog.

_____ 18. The night was so cold that all our pipes had froze.

_____ 19. The policeman shined his light into the store window.

_____ 20. Our captain dove into the river from the bridge.

PUNCTUATION

I. <u>Comma</u>

   A. A comma is used to separate main clauses of medium length joined by *and, but, for, or, neither,* or *nor.*

     1. The books have finally been printed, and you should be able to buy one next Friday.

     2. Most of the girls are going to the movies, but Ann and I are going to study.

     3. You cannot play that record today, for it has been lost.

     4. Neither of the men can play golf today, nor can they tomorrow.

   B. Long introductory phrases or clauses are set off by commas.

     1. Although the instructor was absent, the class was well conducted.

     2. After Mr. Landon and I had chatted for some time about the price of beef, we left the office.

     3. When you are able to save a little, why not invest in savings bonds?

     4. To learn the average income of the class of '30, we sent each alumnus a questionnaire.

     5. Shrugging his shoulders in an indifferent manner, Charles said nothing.

   C. Use commas to set off nonrestrictive modifiers (words, phrases, and clauses). Do not use commas to set off restrictive modifiers.

     1. A fountain pen that scratches is of little use. (restrictive)

     2. My fountain pen, which always scratches, cannot be repaired. (nonrestrictive)

     3. The street that runs in front of my house is paved. (restrictive)

4. Adams Street, that runs in front of my house, is paved. (nonrestrictive)

D. A comma is used between a statement and a question depending upon the statement.

1. You are coming, aren't you?
2. I enjoyed the movie, didn't you?
3. I have turned in my route sheets, have you?

E. In direct quotation words like *he said* are set off by commas.

1. "When I was younger," he said, "I could run six blocks without effort."
2. "I can guarantee this," the salesman said; "our firm is known for its fairness in these matters."

Note. A semicolon is used between clauses of a compound sentence not joined by a conjunction. A period and capital letter would be used ordinarily.

F. Words, phrases, and clauses used in a series are separated by commas.

1. The chief colors in the garden were pink, blue, white, and red.
2. She rose, leaned against the table, and presented her story.
3. The hose should be of long length, of sheer weight, and of a light color.

G. Two adjectives modifying the same noun should be separated by a comma if they are equal in rank; if the word *and* cannot be supplied logically between the adjectives, a comma is used.

1. A faithful, sincere friend.
2. A big gray cat. (not of equal rank)
3. A long, hard winter.

H. In a series of the form a, b, and c, a comma should precede the conjunction.

1. There are blue, white, and yellow dots in your dress.
2. Is this dress green, yellow, or blue?
3. The celery, onions, and radishes are on the table.

Note. In journalistic writing, the comma is usually omitted before the conjunction in a series.

I. A comma is used to separate the successive items of addresses, dates, references, and geographical names.

    1. My address is 1839 North Syracuse Avenue, Minneapolis, Minnesota.

    2. I went to church Sunday, May 18, 1936.

    3. This quotation is from *Julius Caesar, III, 1.*

J. A substantive used in direct address is set off by commas.

    1. Yes, Mary, you may come.

    2. Your guess, my friend, was incorrect.

    3. James, come here.

    4. Come here, sir.

K. An appositive is set off by commas.

    1. We motored to Newport, a beach resort, yesterday.

    2. She introduced her mother, Mrs. Jones.

Note. A restrictive appositive, one that distinguishes its principal from others of its same class, is not usually set off by commas.

    1. The poet Masefield.

    2. Richard the Lion-Hearted.

    3. My sister Johanna.

L. Absolute phrases are set off by commas.

    1. It seems queer, the affair being so late, that he should be tardy.

    2. The tires being smooth, we drove slowly.

    3. I doubt whether she will come, it being so late.

M. Parenthetic words, phrases, or clauses are set off by commas.

    1. But, also, she did not arrive.

    2. The book was, I believe, on the table.

    3. This noon, for example, the lunch was late.

    4. The book was, to tell the truth, none too popular.

N. After an interjection which is intended to be only mildly exclamatory, use a comma rather than an exclamation point.

    1. Oh, she will get well.

    2. Well, come when you are able.

    3. No, you have no right to move that piece.

O. A phrase or clause which is separated from the word that it modifies is set off by commas.

    1. She ran down the street, screaming fearfully.

2. He arrived in Portland Sunday morning, several hours after his scheduled arrival.

3. She answered the teacher's question, looking down at her desk in embarrassment.

II. Semicolon

A. Use a semicolon between two independent clauses whenever these clauses are not joined by a conjunction.

1. Mary went to Salem; I went to Eugene.

2. We must get the ice cream now; without it there would be no dessert.

3. She didn't go to Portland; she went to Seattle.

4. Books which I have recently read are James Michener's *The Bridges of Toko-Ri*, De Voto's *The Course of Empire*, and Alan Paton's *Too Late the Phalarope*; they were fascinating books.

B. A semicolon is used between two independent clauses connected by a conjunctive adverb.

1. We heard that the battle was lost; consequently we prepared to move.

2. She asked if we were comfortable; then she left to get the key.

3. I saw no reason for doing nothing; therefore I read a book.

C. A semicolon is used to separate units that contain smaller elements separated by commas if there is a possibility of misreading.

1. The opera company consisted of Miss Rose, soprano; Miss Albert, alto; Mr. Boz, bass; and Mr. Lune, baritone.

2. If I were a millionaire, I would have horses, automobiles, country estates, yachts; and the whole world should minister to my pleasure.

3. A circular, graveled drive, hedged with spirea and overhung by weeping willows, sweeps leisurely up to the house from the highway; and surrounding it is a four-acre park of groves, and gardens, and lawn.

III. Colon

A. Use a colon to show that something is to follow.

1. There are three reasons for failure: laziness, inability, or misunderstanding.
2. Jane repeated the professor's words: "There shall be no picnic during the time classes assemble."
3. He regarded the demand for popular rights as a king might regard it: that is, as a mode of usurption.

B. A colon may be used after the salutation of a business letter.

1. Dear Sir:
2. Dear Madam:
3. Gentlemen:

C. A colon is used between the parts of titles, references, and numerals.

1. *The Ordeal of Richard Feverel:* a History of a Father and Son.
2. Proverbs 28:20.
3. 7:19 A.M.

D. A colon is used between two clauses of a compound sentence when the second is either an illustration of the first, a restatement in different terms, or sometimes an amplification of the first.

1. Everything was perfect for the fishing trip: the weather was warm, our tackle and poles were new, and our party consisted of a congenial group.
2. The book deserves a short description. It is a novel: it is natural: it contains good portrayals of human characters.
3. The girl was tired: she had cleaned the house.

E. A colon may be used to introduce a long, formal quotation, or when no verb of saying is used.

1. Concerning this matter, Mr. Bryce says: "A further consequence of this habit is pointed out by one of the most thoughtful . . ."
2. He hesitated a moment: "I will make no statement until I have consulted my lawyer."
3. She braced herself against the desk: "I cannot forgive this intrusion."

IV. <u>Dash</u>

A. The dash is used to indicate a decided interruption such as a sudden or unexpected shift in the construction, or a marked break in the thought, or uncertainty or hesitation on the part of the speaker.

1. "She behaved like—" but I could go no further.

2. "Ah! Mr. Sheppard, how—you up from the country? How's your friend—the—er—painter?"

3. If the scythe is rusty—by the way, did you get that scythe at Brown's?

B. Use a dash before a sentence element summarizing the preceding part of a sentence or to heighten suspense and emphasize an appositive.

1. That he has been negligent in attending to his duties; that he is lacking in the qualities necessary for an executive; that he has willfully disregarded instructions—all these charges have been brought against the manager.

2. The waiting, the watching, the hundreds of small necessary acts about the sickroom—all this was past.

C. Use a dash to emphasize a parenthesis or appositive.

1. Society—she knew, she must know—cared little for the forms, the outside things.

2. Editorial writers have severely criticized our policy—or lack of it—on the treatment of our colonies.

3. Ah, yes, he was polite—polite as a Chesterfield—obsequious in fact.

4. I wish to ask regarding a certain law—the pension law.

V. <u>Period</u>

A. Use a period after every declarative or imperative sentence, including sentence fragments that stand for a complete sentence and indirect questions.

1. Yes.

2. I wonder whether Mary will arrive this morning.

3. I am going to the movies this evening.

B. Use a period after every abbreviation except contractions, Roman numerals, and certain other words or initials.

Mr., Dr., Oreg., Col., etc., TVA, II, don't, 12th

C. Always place the period inside the quotation marks and inside the parenthesis when the enclosed material is a complete sentence.

1. I enjoy reading Browning's "My Last Duchess."

2. She answered the door in her slippers. (Her shoes were lost.)

3. I am enclosing thirty dollars ($30).

D. A series of three periods may be used to indicate a break or a change in thought in the dialogue.

1. I'm sorry, but . . .

2. I'm sorry . . . terribly sorry . . . but you . . .

3. "Oh, I don't think . . ." he began.

VI. <u>Exclamation Mark</u>

A. The exclamation point is used after an exclamatory word or sentence.

1. "Ouch!"

2. Oh! You little rascal!

VII. <u>Question Mark</u>

A. The question mark is used after an interrogative sentence or a question of any sort.

1. Is your coat lost?

2. What? You can't mean that.

B. The question mark is placed in parenthesis after doubtful statements to indicate uncertainty as to their correctness. It is out of place to use this mark as humor or dryness.

1. He was born in Oregon City in 1853 (?).

2. Geoffrey Chaucer, 1340 (?)-1400.

C. When a question mark and quotation marks fall together, the question mark is outside if the quoted sentence is not the question, inside if the quoted sentence is the question.

1. "When are you coming home?" she said.

2. Did you really say, "I thought you were older than that"?

D. Use a question mark at the end of each interrogative element in a compound question if separate emphasis is to be given to each of the elements.

           1.   What do you think now of his boasted honor? his integrity? his upright character?

VIII.   <u>Parentheses and Brackets</u>

    A.   Parentheses are used to enclose material that is remotely related to the context.

           1.   This book (I hope you have read it by now) will be discussed in class Tuesday.

    B.   Parentheses are used to enclose various explanations, references, and directions to the reader, and the divisions of an enumeration within the sentence.

           1.   In the following year (1905) he left.

           2.   The subject of taxes (see chapter III) is in need of review.

    C.   Brackets are used to enclose a correction, to indicate material that is supplied, or to call attention to an error.

           1.   Joe said, "I took this for granite [granted]."

           2.   "The commanding officer [Smith] was responsible," said the private.

           3.   "You was [sic] not the man he was . . ."

IX.   <u>Quotation Marks</u>

    A.   Quotation marks are used to enclose direct quotations, not indirect quotations, however.

           1.   "I will see you soon," he said.

           2.   "Are you coming?" I asked.

    B.   Quotation marks are used to enclose the title of a chapter or article in a book or magazine when the names of both the larger and the smaller unit occur in the same passage. The title of the complete work is in italics.

           1.   I refer you to the article on "Industries at War" in the June *Reader's Digest.*

           2.   See. W. F. Jacobs' "A Week in Tahiti" in *Journeys in the South Seas.*

    C.   When a quotation is divided, each of the parts is enclosed by a separate set of quotation marks.

           1.   "Don't you believe me?" I cried in despair. "I am telling you nothing but the truth."

           2.   "There is only one name on this card that appeals to me," I said. "Manager."

           3.   "And now," Henry said, beaming, "I must leave you for a few minutes."

X.   <u>Capitalization</u>

    A.   Capitalize the following:

           1.   Proper names and titles:

James V, St. Louis, the Geology Department, Mississippi River, Alexander the Great, Edward Spencer, Ph.D., Reverend Jones, Thirteenth Avenue, Professor Smith, a Ford.

2. First word of a sentence or line of poetry:

3. Days of the week, months, and holidays:

   October, August, Thanksgiving, Monday

4. Organizations, corporations, churches, societies, political parties and members of such organizations or bodies:

   Republican Party, United States Steel Corporation, the Methodist Church, the Red Cross, Democrats, Catholics, Masons

5. Historical events and documents:

   The Middle Ages, the Magna Carta, the Battle of Waterloo, the Bill of Rights

6. Geographical regions:

   the West, Northern California, the Southwest

7. Names of the Deity:

   God, the Lord, the Savior, the Holy Ghost

8. Names of nationalities, races, and languages:

   Roman, Spanish, Negro, White, English

9. Important words in titles of books, articles, poems, and compositions:

   The Story of a Bad Boy, *Abe Lincoln in Illinois*, *Rhapsody in Blue*

10. The first word of a direct quotation:

    Mother said, "My dear, it is time to get up." The sheriff shouted, "Halt," and pointed his gun.

B. Do not capitalize the following:

1. Common nouns: east, maple, river, avenue

2. Names of the seasons, unless personified: summer, fall, autumn, but "O wild West Wind, thou breath of Autumn's being."

3. Courses of study, unless a particular course is named: biology, civics, geography, but Biology 311, Economics 263

XI. <u>Hyphen</u>

A. When suggested by the dictionary, use a hyphen between parts of a compound word: great-grandfather, self-sacrifice, mother-in-law, ex-president, pro-British, air-conditioned, twenty-one, ninety-nine, two-thirds.

B.   Use a hyphen when two or more words are used as a single adjective preceding the word they modify; well-knit frame, tight-fitting coat, old-fashioned dress, never-to-be-forgotten moment, light-complexioned girl, one-inch board, two- and three-inch boards. Note: No hyphen is used when these words follow the noun. His frame was well knit. The girl was light complexioned.

C.   At the end of a line use a hyphen to indicate a broken word. Divide only between syllables.

XII.   Italics

A.   Italics (indicated by underlining) are generally used for names of ships and aircraft, for titles of books and plays, for magazines and newspapers, and for musical compositions and works of art.

XIII.   Apostrophe

A.   The apostrophe is used to indicate the omission of one or more letters or one or more figures from a word or date: can't, don't, won't, it's, 'tis, I'd, ass'n, o'clock, class of '59.

B.   The apostrophe is generally used to form the plural of letters, figures, signs, and words used as words: a's, 4's, &'s, t's, i's, and's, but's.

C.   The apostrophe and s are usually added to form the possessive case: cat's paw, Cross's dog, Charles's book, the fox's trail, the Women's Organization, Keats's poetry, Wordsworth's sonnets, Meier and Frank's store. If the word ends in an s-sound, and the addition of an additional s-sound would make the pronunciation awkward, omit the final s and end the word with an apostrophe only: the Crosses' car, Aristophanes' comedies, Ulysses' bow, the Andrews' baby, foxes' holes.

D.   The apostrophe is used with *sake* in such expressions as conscience' sake, heaven's sake, righteousness' sake.

E.   The apostrophe is used with certain idioms of time, measure, rate, or worth: hour's delay, two hours' delay (but usually a two-week vacation), a stone's throw, a hand's breadth, a moment's wait, a dollar's worth, seventy-five cents' worth.

F.   The apostrophe is used with a double possessive: that book of John's, those sonnets of Keats's.

G.   The apostrophe is used with a possessive noun (i.e. a possessive adjective) preceding a gerund. I could not understand Henry's making such an error.

Exercises for

1. PUNCTUATION

Directions: Supply commas wherever needed. Then in the blanks before each sentence write in order the letters that represent the rule. Write _f_ if no comma is needed.

    a. comma used to separate main clauses
    b. comma used after introductory words
    c. comma used to set off nonrestrictive elements
    d. comma used in a series
    e. comma used with items of dates and addresses
    f. no comma needed

____ 1. When I could distinguish the sharp-cut[1] inky[2] borders of the trees outside the window[3] I knew that day was not far off.

____ 2. Barefoot and leisurely[1] he strolled up the path from the gate to the terrace—a tall[2] bearded[3] Galla in a white _chamma_ bordered with the Prophet's green.

____ 3. After the August vacation hordes have shaken the sand out of their shoes and departed[1] this popular seaside resort normally sinks into a silence of closed hotels[2] stacked café chairs[3] and promenades deserted by everything but the west wind.

____ 4. It was my birthday[1] and on the bureau[2] was a present from an uncle[3] whom I do not remember.

____ 5. As she began to talk to me earnestly[1] I found that[2] her questions were not as bad as those of her husband[3] who wears a beard.

____ 6. Turning to her with a toothy smile[1] Violet asked if it were true that she had come to St. Louis[2] Missouri[3] from Tennessee.

____ 7. As she tapped her stubby fingers on the window sill[1] my landlady[2] who seldom was awake when I left[3] requested that I pay my rent immediately.

____ 8. Any man[1] who has not wished for a red convertible[2] is very unusual[3] and you should mark him well.

Exercises for

2. PUNCTUATION

Directions: Supply commas wherever needed. Then in the blanks before each sentence write in order the letters that represent the rule. Write *f* if no comma is needed.

- a. comma in direct address
- b. comma with appositives
- c. comma with absolute phrases
- d. comma with parenthetical elements
- e. comma with phrase or clause separated from the word it modifies
- f. no comma needed

— — — 1. I had known only one rival$_1$ a young man two years my senior$_2$ named$_3$ of all things, Mergatroyd Smithpeter.

— — — 2. James Orville$_1$ a very gentle and businesslike man$_2$ of forty-one$_3$ had immediately apologized for his remarks.

— — — 3. His only friend was a youth$_1$ a little older than he$_2$ a boxer named Martin Watkins$_3$ who also frequented the gymnasium.

— — — 4. Into his office one afternoon$_1$ came a dear$_2$ old lady$_3$ Mrs. Margaret Benson.

— — — 5. The inspector said, "You are at liberty$_1$ sir$_2$ to give your account$_3$ taking strict care to tell the complete truth."

— — — 6. The manager$_1$ having promised us some heat$_2$ we sat huddled in our coats$_3$ our breath steaming in the cold.

— — — 7. Tell me$_1$ Major Buckingham$_2$ have you ever been shot at$_3$ or wounded?

— —.— — 8. You must know$_1$ of course$_2$ that such things are not tolerated at Carver$_3$ the school with a reputation.

— — — 9. Sue$_1$ you may search through the documents again, but$_2$ of course$_3$ you will find nothing.

— — — 10. "Good morning$_1$ Judge," said Mr. Wilson$_2$ smiling with all his teeth$_3$ and placing his brief case on the table.

Exercises for

3. PUNCTUATION

Directions: Supply punctuation wherever needed. Then in the blanks before each sentence write in order the letters that represent the punctuation you have supplied. Write *e* if no mark of punctuation is needed.

a. comma
b. semicolon
c. quotation marks

d. apostrophe in preceding word
e. no punctuation needed
f. hyphen

_ _ _ _ _ 1. Worn and exhausted$_1$ he leaned upon his rifle$_2$ and shook his gaunt hand fiercely at the silent$_3$ widespread$_4$ city beneath him.

_ _ _ _ _ 2. The Storys$_1$ were not even from the South$_2$ like the Lumkins they were from$_3$ Pittsburgh$_4$ Pennsylvania.

_ _ _ _ _ 3. He was a brave man$_1$ but he trembled at the vague$_2$ shadowy$_3$ terrors$_4$ which hung over him.

_ _ _ _ _ 4. The ladies$_1$ creeping home from lunch in their electric cars squeezed one anothers$_2$ white$_3$ gloved hands$_4$ and repeated what Miss White had said.

_ _ _ _ _ 5. There was no living creature near the remains of the fire$_1$ animals$_2$ man$_3$ maiden$_4$ all were gone.

_ _ _ _ _ 6. His face was lean$_1$ and haggard$_2$ and the brown$_3$ parchment$_4$ like skin was drawn tightly over the projecting bones.

_ _ _ _ _ 7. She even bought an apple$_1$ green convertible$_2$ with it she visited Hot Springs$_3$ Arkansas, and Pineville$_4$ Tennessee.

_ _ _ _ _ 8. "We are at a loss to know,$_1$ he said, "how he came into the almost$_2$ empty house$_3$ indeed$_4$ the whole affair is puzzling."

_ _ _ _ _ 9. Aunt Mandy's three$_1$ layer chocolate cake$_2$ which was covered with thick white frosting$_3$ was displayed on the table in all its$_4$ glory.

Exercises for

4. PUNCTUATION

Directions: Supply punctuation wherever needed. Then in the blanks before each sentence write in order the letters that represent the punctuation you have supplied. Write _e_ if no mark of punctuation is needed.

a. comma
b. semicolon
c. quotation marks

d. apostrophe in preceding word
e. no punctuation needed
f. hyphen

_____ 1. The Presbyterian manse has a black₁ iron fence with four₂ sided pillars like tall₃ thin₄ bird cages.

_____ 2. Twitching the navy-blue skirt with her thin white hands₁ she said desperately₂ ₃I don't know₄ what they are wearing anymore."

_____ 3. Neither of us₁ is really listening₂ to what he is saying₃ we are listening for sounds₄ from upstairs.

_____ 4. One day in May, 1929₁ the three ladies and a man came to lunch at Mrs. Rockerfellers₂ ₃he was A. Conjur Goodyear₄ who was a wealthy collector.

_____ 5. The men on the sidewalk are young₁ limber₂ sharp₃ faced₄ almost insolent young men.

_____ 6. The moonlight₁ which seems so lucid and brilliant when you look up₂ is all pearl₃ and smoke round the pond₄ and the hills.

_____ 7. The very day before "Rio Rita" gets under-way₁ the Kinkajou has pillaged and burned the ranch of Rio Rita₂ a local senorita₃ and her brother₄ who was named Roberto.

_____ 8. "Oh," he said₁ "pardon me₂ Mr. Henry₃ I didnt₄ know you had company."

_____ 9. On the whole₁ the conference gave a general impression₂ of caution on the platform₃ and a fog of confusion₄ on the floor.

Exercises for

5. PUNCTUATION

Directions: Supply punctuation wherever needed. Then in the blanks before each sentence write in order the letters that represent the punctuation you have supplied. Write *e* if no mark of punctuation is needed.

a. comma
b. semicolon
c. quotation marks

d. apostrophe in preceding word
e. no punctuation needed
f. hyphen

_____ 1. "I wonder what that fellow is looking for?" I asked₁ pointing to a stalwart₂ plainly₃ dressed individual₄ who was walking slowly down the other side of the street.

_____ 2. "Lecoq was a miserable bungler,₁ he said₂ in an angry voice₃ "he had only one thing to recommend him₄ and that was his energy."

_____ 3. There was one sallow₁ rat-faced₂ dark₃ eyed fellow₄ who was introduced to me as Mr. Leslie.

_____ 4. Flossie had set up her drawing board in the Woods₁ study₂ and very soon she had completed for herself₃ a coat of arms which hung in the library₄ before long she was constantly engaged in this type of work.

_____ 5. It was a foggy₁ cloudy₂ morning₃ and a dun-colored veil hung over the house-tops, looking like the reflection of the mud₄ colored streets beneath.

_____ 6. William kept his room in perfect order₁ and never had to be told₂ to comb his hair₃ or wash his hands₄ or put on a clean shirt.

_____ 7. "Tell me about your little nephews₁ I understand youre₂ very fond of them,₃ remarked Mr. Medford₄ seating himself on the green sofa.

Exercises for

6. PUNCTUATION

Directions: Supply punctuation wherever needed. Then in the blanks before each sentence write in order the letters that represent the punctuation you have supplied. Write *e* if no mark of punctuation is needed.

a. comma
b. semicolon
c. quotation marks

d. apostrophe in preceding word
e. no punctuation needed
f. hyphen

— — — — 1. Ahead₁ the road is lined with dark₂ thin₃ old elms₄ grass grows long and rank in the ditches.

— — — — 2. ₁Stand up now and lets₂ see how tall you are₃ ₄she tells me.

— — — — 3. "Why"₁ said Williams,₂ even the jewelry sold in the Japanese auction stores is not genuine₃ and the sellers are not Japanese.₄

— — — — 4. Beyond the house₁ lay the farm—three block₂ long rows of brooder houses and their yards₃ foaming with a raucous multitude of half₄ grown chickens.

— — — — 5. On one side it is bordered with birch₁ oak₂ maple₃ hickory₄ and occasional groups of hemlocks.

— — — — 6. "Well₁ if you people are going to work₂ Ill₃ sit down and read"₄ Mrs. Noble said.

— — — — 7. He that runs may read₁ nor have there been wanting₂ attentive₃ and malicious observers₄ to point this out.

— — — — 8. They were not men₁ of letters₂ they were₃ as a body₄ unpopular.

— — — — 9. The officer said to Mr. Tripp,₁ Theres₂ something wrong here," and Mr. Tripp answered, "Yes₃ I think theres₄ something wrong here."

Exercises for

7. PUNCTUATION

Direction: Supply punctuation wherever needed. Then in the blanks before each sentence write in order the letters that represent the punctuation you have supplied. Write *e* if no mark of punctuation or capitalization is needed.

a. comma
b. semicolon
c. capital letter

d. quotation marks
e. no punctuation or capitalization needed

_____ 1. People$_1$ who wanted to cash checks$_2$ without visiting a bank$_3$ came to him$_4$ for he always kept a large amount of money in his safe.

_____ 2. She might have continued to attend$_1$ law school$_2$ however she had fallen in love with a young man$_3$ who was eager to get married$_4$ and move to California.

_____ 3. "You are to be congratulated,$_1$ I remarked$_2$ considerably surprised at his enthusiasm$_3$ $_4$I know that you will be very happy."

_____ 4. Langdon, my wife's cousin$_1$ smiled sweetly$_2$ and said$_3$ that he had never tried to keep the affair secret$_4$ nor would he object to having it made known.

_____ 5. Miss Virginia's stories were always about the past$_1$ about the old plantation$_2$ about the slaves$_3$ and about the glories of the $_4$south.

_____ 6. The Willamette $_1$river flows$_2$ north to join the Columbia at Portland$_3$ Oregon$_4$ the largest city in the state.

_____ 7. When his new $_1$ford automobile knocked down a young $_2$elm tree in front of my house$_3$ I asked, "Have you ever driven a car before?$_4$

_____ 8. She had been swept off her feet by Thomas Blade$_1$ the black $_2$sheep of the family$_3$ this proved a serious mistake$_4$ and one she regretted all her life.

61

Exercises for

8. PUNCTUATION

Directions: Supply punctuation wherever needed. Then in the blanks before each sentence write in order the letters that represent the punctuation you have supplied. Write *e* if no mark of punctuation or capitalization is needed.

a. comma
b. semicolon
c. capital letter

d. question mark
e. no punctuation or capitalization needed

————— 1. "When you went to the ₁south for the ₂summer₃ why did you not visit a doctor₄" asked Mrs. Morris.

————— 2. May I take ₁history 201, ₂professor Marl₃ I am interested in the ₄renaissance?

————— 3. My Uncle Wellmore was born on March 21₁ 1899₂ in a log cabin on the Metton ₃river in the ₄midwest.

————— 4. "Did French ₁canadians from the Hudson's Bay ₂company settle in this region₃" my ₄grandfather asked.

————— 5. The ₁oak and ₂elm trees had been planted by ₃professor Wood on the hill top₄ there they grew for a hundred years.

————— 6. Many a ₁southern woman in a ₂northern ₃city comes to regard ₄negroes in a different light.

————— 7. I am taking ₁latin, ₂physics₃ and ₄biology this semester.

————— 8. The ₁graduate student had amassed a great amount of out-of-the-way knowledge about the ₂reformation₃ however he had made no systematic study of the ₄movement.

————— 9. "Do you know that the Mackenzie ₁river flows ₂north₃" asked Dr. Jensen, ₄professor of geography.

————— 10. The Methodist ₁church in Plumville was built in 1886₂ it was dedicated on ₃november ₄tenth of that year.

9. PUNCTUATION

Directions: Punctuate the following sentences; then circle the number or numbers that identify the punctuation you have supplied.

1. apostrophe
2. comma
3. semicolon

4. quotation marks
5. colon
6. question mark

1 2 3 4 5 6   1. This is not my book but you may read it if you like.

1 2 3 4 5 6   2. Jean removed from the sidewalk the paper which James hadnt bothered to remove.

1 2 3 4 5 6   3. When you have read this book will you have any new ideas on life.

1 2 3 4 5 6   4. Jean never admitted however that she had been engaged for a week.

1 2 3 4 5 6   5. They did the first six furlongs in 1 04.5 this is extraordinary time for two-year-olds at Pimlico isnt it.

1 2 3 4 5 6   6. At the milldam the hockey game still rages the players take no heed of the noon train.

1 2 3 4 5 6   7. Well when a man begins to moralize said his wife its time to go home.

1 2 3 4 5 6   8. I have known the shock of young men who look like kings of Wall Street and speak like shoe clerks.

1 2 3 4 5 6   9. My village is I think a special favorite of the President's.

1 2 3 4 5 6 10. The motion is like flying in a dream you float free and the world floats under you.

1 2 3 4 5 6 11. Around him was his room the modest sitting room of an assistant professor.

1 2 3 4 5 6 12. I believe you son my grandfather said gravely.

1 2 3 4 5 6 13. The children were in bed when we left they would be in bed when we got back.

1 2 3 4 5 6 14. Having ceased from the heavy farm work he noted the reappearance of an old fraility he began to cough again.

1 2 3 4 5 6 15. Madam will you have dinner now asked the young man.

10. PUNCTUATION

<u>*Directions:*</u> Punctuate the following sentences; then circle the number or numbers that identify the punctuation you have supplied.

1. apostrophe
2. comma
3. semicolon
4. quotation marks
5. colon
6. question mark

1 2 3 4 5 6   1. If you have an answer notify me at 328 South Second Street Salem Oregon before July 5.

1 2 3 4 5 6   2. Jane Gretz who had fallen from a horse when she was six was opposed to riding.

1 2 3 4 5 6   3. She wouldnt admit that she was guilty she was afraid of the consequences.

1 2 3 4 5 6   4. Joseph made the following statement It is possible for anyone who tries to pass this test.

1 2 3 4 5 6   5. Replying that she would not go Mary ran from the room.

1 2 3 4 5 6   6. Yes I am able to say that she will come to our meeting however I dont believe her suggestions will be very valuable.

1 2 3 4 5 6   7. When my father went fishing in the Columbia River he caught one small salmon.

1 2 3 4 5 6   8. This classroom is very full isnt it.

1 2 3 4 5 6   9. Today we will start the show said Mr. Jones and all those who come will be given a picture of the leading lady.

1 2 3 4 5 6   10. My mother wrote me that my brother would soon be home.

1 2 3 4 5 6   11. Is it all right for me to welcome him she asked I dont want to do the wrong thing.

1 2 3 4 5 6   12. She was given the opportunity of going to Chicago to study but she refused it.

1 2 3 4 5 6   13. Does anyone own this dog she questioned.

1 2 3 4 5 6   14. In your themes the instructor said I want the following things unity coherence emphasis interest.

1 2 3 4 5 6   15. May I give these notes to the members who were not here.

SPELLING

Spelling may cause you more difficulty than anything else in your composition classes. You will be helped by learning to consult a good college-level dictionary whenever you are in doubt about the spelling of a word. Recommended dictionaries are *Webster's New Collegiate Dictionary*, published by the G. & C. Merriam Company, *The American College Dictionary*, published by Harper & Brothers, and *Webster's New World Dictionary*, College Edition, published by The World Publishing Company.

You will need to keep a list of the words that *you* commonly misspell. It may be that you seldom misspell the words on spelling lists, but may still make many errors in other words. These are your troublesome words, and you should study your list frequently and add to it words that you cannot spell.

Finally, careful study of the following list of simple words frequently misspelled will help you to become a better speller. You should read each word aloud to see that you are giving it the correct pronunciation. You should know its meaning. Then you should practice spelling the word *until you cannot be confused*.

absence	arguing	cemetery
accept	awkward	changeable
accidentally	bachelor	clothes
accommodate	barbarous	committee
accumulate	battalion	concede
acknowledgment	beggar	conferred
acquainted	believe	conquer
across	benefited	conqueror
aisle	biscuit	conscience
all right	Britain	conscientious
analyze	bureau	consensus
apology	burglar	courteous
apparatus	calendar	dealt
apparent	candidate	dependence

descendant
desperate
dilemma
dining
disappear
disappoint
disastrous
disease
dissipate
divine
dormitories
ecstasy
eighth
embarrass
equipped
equipment
exaggerate
exceed
exhilarate
existence
familiar
feminine
fiery
financier
forceful
forcible
forehead
foreign
foremost
fragile
frantically
fundamental
ghastly
ghost
governor
grievous
guard
harass
height
heir
hindrance
hoping
humorous

hypnotize
hypocrisy
illegible
inadvisable
incidentally
incompatible
incredible
incredulous
independence
indescribable
indispensable
inevitable
innocence
inoculate
instance
instant
laboratory
lacquer
leisure
liable
lieutenant
lightning
loneliness
lying
maintenance
maneuver
manufacturer
Massachusetts
mathematics
miniature
mischievous
misspelled
mortgage
mosquito
murmur
negligible
Negroes
noticeable
occasion
occur
occurred
omit
omitted

optimistic
originate
outrageous
pamphlet
parallel
paralyze
parenthesis
parliament
partner
pastime
pendulum
perform
persuade
pertinent
physical
physician
picnic
picnicking
plateau
politician
prairie
preference
preferred
preparatory
primitive
proceed
professor
psychology
pursue
pyramid
quizzes
recede
receipt
receive
recognize
reign
Renaissance
repetition
rheumatism
rhythm
ridiculous
sandwich
schedule

seize
sensible
separate
sergeant
shriek
siege
similar
sincerely
sophomore
specimen
strictly
subtle

succeed
superintendent
supersede
surprise
susceptible
syllable
temperament
temperature
thorough
tragedy
tries
Tuesday

until
usage
usually
village
villain
Wednesday
weird
wiry
women
writing
yacht

Exercises for

1. SPELLING

Directions: In the space at the left write the number that corresponds to any misspelled word. If no word is misspelled, leave the space blank. No more than one misspelled word appears in any one line.

_____ 1. 1 temperament   2 forcable   3 plateau   4 picnic

_____ 2. 1 height   2 incidentally   3 independence   4 cematery

_____ 3. 1 believe   2 physician   3 primitive   4 shriek

_____ 4. 1 ridiculous   2 sandwich   3 exstacy   4 desperate

_____ 5. 1 schedule   2 omit   3 minature   4 incredulous

_____ 6. 1 hoping   2 incompatible   3 courteous   4 humerous

_____ 7. 1 bachelor   2 exhilarate   3 accept   4 analyze

_____ 8. 1 grievious   2 fundamental   3 bureau   4 calendar

_____ 9. 1 exaggerate   2 lieing   3 dormitories   4 villain

_____ 10. 1 preferred   2 pendulum   3 trys   4 preference

_____ 11. 1 wierd   2 quizzes   3 governor   4 maintenance

_____ 12. 1 harass   2 outrageous   3 originate   4 alright

_____ 13. 1 lacquer   2 noticeable   3 paralyze   4 occurred

_____ 14. 1 Wednesday   2 syllable   3 Renaissance   4 sophmore

_____ 15. 1 supersede   2 reign   3 rhumatism   4 conscience

_____ 16. 1 conferred   2 apparant   3 barbarous   4 repetition

_____ 17. 1 psychology   2 superintendent   3 Tuesday   4 politician

_____ 18. 1 receive   2 subtle   3 incredible   4 innocence

_____ 19. 1 omitted   2 acknowledgement   3 inoculate   4 laboratory

_____ 20. 1 clothes   2 fiery   3 changeable   4 professor

_____ 21. 1 forceful   2 aisle   3 maneuver   4 incompatible

_____ 22. 1 occasion   2 receipt   3 perform   4 acumulate

_____ 23. 1 pertinent   2 tragedy   3 Negros   4 pursue

_____ 24. 1 conscientious   2 equipped   3 frantically   4 pasttime

_____ 25. 1 procede   2 existence   3 feminine   4 embarrass

71

Exercises for

2. SPELLING

Directions: In the space at the left write the number that corresponds to any misspelled word. If no word is misspelled, leave the space blank. No more than one misspelled word appears in any one line .

_____ 1. 1 disease   2 dissipate   3 comittee   4 forehead

_____ 2. 1 prairie   2 foriegn   3 usually   4 rhythm

_____ 3. 1 recognize   2 proceed   3 ghastly   4 leisure

_____ 4. 1 independence   2 laboratory   3 Massachusetts   4 batalion

_____ 5. 1 mathematics   2 conqueror   3 awkwurd   4 arguing

_____ 6. 1 Britian   2 fragile   3 eighth   4 conscience

_____ 7. 1 equipped   2 dependence   3 benefited   4 partner

_____ 8. 1 mischievous   2 liable   3 delt   4 hindrance

_____ 9. 1 lying   2 femanine   3 omit   4 supersede

_____ 10. 1 pyramid   2 seize   3 physical   4 disasterous

_____ 11. 1 candadate   2 tries   3 specimen   4 loneliness

_____ 12. 1 pursue   2 sandwich   3 weird   4 hypnotize

_____ 13. 1 divine   2 equippment   3 disappoint   4 all right

_____ 14. 1 usage   2 reign   3 pursue   4 illegable

_____ 15. 1 physical   2 schedule   3 burgular   4 recede

_____ 16. 1 receive   2 sensible   3 dinning   4 succeed

_____ 17. 1 women   2 village   3 strictly   4 acquainted

_____ 18. 1 sergeant   2 sincerely   3 inevitable   4 loneliness

_____ 19. 1 mortgage   2 indescribable   3 mosquito   4 ridiculous

_____ 20. 1 concensus   2 physician   3 similar   4 inadvisable

_____ 21. 1 parallel   2 lightening   3 occur   4 hpyocrisy

_____ 22. 1 maneuver   2 changeable   3 embarrass   4 financier

_____ 23. 1 occassion   2 forcible   3 courteous   4 apology

_____ 24. 1 fundamental   2 optimistic   3 murmur   4 noticeable

_____ 25. 1 incidentally   2 dissappear   3 grievous   4 miniature

Exercises for

3. SPELLING

Directions: In the space at the left write the number that corresponds to any misspelled word. If no word is misspelled, leave the space blank. No more than one misspelled word appears in any one line.

_____ 1. 1 disappear   2 prairie   3 heighth   4 familiar

_____ 2. 1 useage   2 feminine   3 divine   4 pursue

_____ 3. 1 recognize   2 conquer   3 accomodate   4 committee

_____ 4. 1 syllable   2 temperament   3 maneuver   4 equipment

_____ 5. 1 disastrous   2 instant   3 concede   4 acquainted

_____ 6. 1 preform   2 omitted   3 ghastly   4 susceptible

_____ 7. 1 tries   2 subtle   3 ridiculous   4 mermur

_____ 8. 1 lightning   2 existance   3 descendant   4 aisle

_____ 9. 1 accept   2 disappoint   3 parenthasis   4 fundamental

_____ 10. 1 sandwitch   2 thorough   3 partner   4 parallel

_____ 11. 1 forceful   2 ecstasy   3 mathamatics   4 proceed

_____ 12. 1 wiry   2 indispensable   3 succeed   4 lonliness

_____ 13. 1 conscience   2 apparent   3 politician   4 occur

_____ 14. 1 maintenance   2 fiery   3 incredable   4 village

_____ 15. 1 siege   2 pyramid   3 dealt   4 cematery

_____ 16. 1 beggar   2 apology   3 sophomore   4 sieze

_____ 17. 1 negligible   2 heir   3 bureau   4 paralyze

_____ 18. 1 yacht   2 manufacturer   3 embarass   4 candidate

_____ 19. 1 Britain   2 originate   3 rheumatism   4 liable

_____ 20. 1 dissippate   2 fragile   3 burglar   4 shriek

_____ 21. 1 repetition   2 mischievous   3 inadvisable   4 formost

_____ 22. 1 hoping   2 morgage   3 governor   4 specimen

_____ 23. 1 separate   2 mosquitoe   3 hypocrisy   4 across

_____ 24. 1 plateau   2 independence   3 franically   4 sensible

_____ 25. 1 rhythm   2 sincerely   3 inoculate   4 superintendant

Exercises for

4. SPELLING

Directions: In the space at the left write the number that corresponds to any misspelled word. If no word is misspelled, leave the space blank. No more than one misspelled word appears in any one line.

_____ 1. 1 accommodate 2 biscuit 3 exhilarate 4 misspelled

_____ 2. 1 negligible 2 parliament 3 ghost 4 Rennaissance

_____ 3. 1 temperature 2 picnicking 3 paralel 4 hindrance

_____ 4. 1 arguing 2 begger 3 instant 4 thorough

_____ 5. 1 yacht 2 reign 3 familar 4 apparatus

_____ 6. 1 dependance 2 accidentally 3 originate 4 incredulous

_____ 7. 1 heir 2 hypnotize 3 noticeable 4 Massachusetts

_____ 8. 1 mosquito 2 dealt 3 acquainted 4 formost

_____ 9. 1 accumulate 2 analize 3 parenthesis 4 hypocrisy

_____ 10. 1 liesure 2 illegible 3 guard 4 omit

_____ 11. 1 occasion 2 devine 3 lacquer 4 committee

_____ 12. 1 conqueror 2 fragile 3 consensus 4 absense

_____ 13. 1 aisle 2 tragedy 3 surprise 4 maintainance

_____ 14. 1 murmer 2 maneuver 3 conscientious 4 forehead

_____ 15. 1 fiery 2 conferred 3 accross 4 burglar

_____ 16. 1 exceed 2 foreign 3 candidate 4 paralyze

_____ 17. 1 occur 2 gastly 3 superintendent 4 succeed

_____ 18. 1 innocence 2 dissipate 3 dilemma 4 wirey

_____ 19. 1 villain 2 seize 3 sincerely 4 inevitable

_____ 20. 1 instance 2 conquer 3 calender 4 disease

_____ 21. 1 pardner 2 fragile 3 separate 4 quizzes

_____ 22. 1 siege 2 pyramid 3 receipt 4 indispensable

_____ 23. 1 humorous 2 incompatable 3 bureau 4 forceful

_____ 24. 1 politican 2 loneliness 3 liable 4 height

_____ 25. 1 strictly 2 repetition 3 rheumatism 4 suttle

Exercises for

5. SPELLING

Directions: In the space at the left write the number that corresponds to any misspelled word. If no word is misspelled, leave the space blank. No more than one misspelled word appears in any one line.

_____ 1.   1 exhilerate   2 thorough   3 persuade   4 yacht

_____ 2.   1 writing   2 rhythm   3 ghost   4 harass

_____ 3.   1 laboratory   2 mathematics   3 barbarous   4 morgage

_____ 4.   1 absence   2 picnicing   3 susceptible   4 recede

_____ 5.   1 sargeant   2 village   3 governor   4 arguing

_____ 6.   1 across   2 women   3 similar   4 pendulum

_____ 7.   1 sophomore   2 grievous   3 omited   4 indescribable

_____ 8.   1 financeir   2 heir   3 exaggerate   4 frantically

_____ 9.   1 syllable   2 plateau   3 hindrance   4 curteous

_____ 10.   1 partner   2 inadvisable   3 parliament   4 biscuit

_____ 11.   1 descendant   2 desperate   3 equipped   4 psychology

_____ 12.   1 manufacturer   2 clothes   3 parenthasis   4 parallel

_____ 13.   1 guard   2 mischievous   3 dissapoint   4 beggar

_____ 14.   1 benefitted   2 apology   3 sensible   4 perform

_____ 15.   1 wiry   2 sincerely   3 physical   4 pertanent

_____ 16.   1 indispensable   2 outrageous   3 useage   4 dormitories

_____ 17.   1 ecstasy   2 fundemental   3 Britain   4 foremost

_____ 18.   1 temperment   2 awkward   3 apparent   4 occurred

_____ 19.   1 outrageous   2 shriek   3 preferred   4 adknowledgment

_____ 20.   1 accept   2 optimistic   3 humorous   4 batchelor

_____ 21.   1 familiar   2 battalion   3 embarass   4 usually

_____ 22.   1 recognize   2 pastime   3 conceed   4 incredible

_____ 23.   1 miniature   2 untill   3 Negroes   4 cemetery

_____ 24.   1 speciman   2 existence   3 changeable   4 eighth

_____ 25.   1 feminine   2 hoping   3 inoculate   4 prarie

Exercises for

6. SPELLING

Directions: In the space at the left write the number that corresponds to any misspelled word. If no word is misspelled, leave the space blank. No more than one misspelled word appears in any one line.

_____ 1. 1 miniature   2 indescribable   3 supersede   4 writting

_____ 2. 1 awkward   2 innocence   3 disease   4 untill

_____ 3. 1 noticable   2 preferred   3 quizzes   4 benefited

_____ 4. 1 pendulum   2 courteous   3 analyze   4 superintendent

_____ 5. 1 eighth   2 Renaissance   3 calendar   4 villian

_____ 6. 1 schedule   2 picnicing   3 outrageous   4 conferred

_____ 7. 1 financier   2 labratory   3 women   4 physician

_____ 8. 1 sergeant   2 conqueror   3 incredulous   4 foreign

_____ 9. 1 Negros   2 Wednesday   3 Tuesday   4 Massachusetts

_____ 10. 1 desperate   2 all right   3 mispelled   4 receive

_____ 11. 1 stricly   2 optimistic   3 primitive   4 dilemma

_____ 12. 1 dormitories   2 batchelor   3 accidentally   4 parliament

_____ 13. 1 acknowledgement   2 usually   3 leisure   4 exceed

_____ 14. 1 occurred   2 incompatible   3 occassion   4 dining

_____ 15. 1 inoculate   2 arguing   3 biscuit   4 temperture

_____ 16. 1 lieutenant   2 grievous   3 hindrance   4 battallion

_____ 17. 1 similiar   2 psychology   3 lacquer   4 exaggerate

_____ 18. 1 ghost   2 harras   3 dependence   4 accumulate

_____ 19. 1 apparatus   2 forcible   3 reign   4 pertinent

_____ 20. 1 persuade   2 incidentally   3 changable   4 conscientious

_____ 21. 1 receipt   2 humorous   3 exhilerate   4 absence

_____ 22. 1 tradgedy   2 pamphlet   3 illegible   4 instance

_____ 23. 1 consensus   2 clothes   3 professor   4 preparatory

_____ 24. 1 surprise   2 forhead   3 inevitable   4 believe

_____ 25. 1 barbarious   2 equipped   3 lying   4 guard

Correct Word Choice

Some words, because they sound alike, cause a great deal of difficulty. Study the following:

accept	I *accept* your invitation.
except	Everyone will be there *except* Jane.
advice (n)	Will you give me some *advice?*
advise (v)	I *advise* you to sell your mining stock.
affect	It does not *affect* me. George had an *affected* (adj.) manner of speaking.
effect	The drug has a powerful *effect*. At last the prisoners *effected* their escape.
all ready	At last the men were *all ready* to go.
already	Sally had *already* gone when I arrived.
all together	The grandchildren were *all together* that Christmas.
altogether	There has been *altogether* too much whispering.
angel	An *angel* appeared to him in a vision.
angle	Please hand me a right-*angle* triangle.
capitol	We looked up at the dome of the *capitol*.
capital	Mr. Pierpont supplied the *capital* for the project. The president discussed the conflict between *capital* and labor.
coarse	*Coarse* gravel was used as a base for the street.
course	You know, of *course*, that this is foolish.
complement	The squad had its full *complement* of men.
compliment	The press paid the actress a high *compliment*.

corps	Sam joined the Signal *Corps*.
corpse	Sherlock Holmes looked down at the *corpse* of the murdered man.
council	The property owners appeared before the city *council*.
counsel	You paid the lawyer for his good *counsel*.
consul	Franklin Pierce appointed him *consul* in Liverpool.
device (n)	His banner bore this strange *device*.
devise (v)	Quickly the general *devised* a new plan of attack.
desert	The camel caravan crossed the *desert*.
dessert	Mother served us pie for *dessert*.
dual	The driver-training car had *dual* controls.
duel	The *duel* was fought with pistols.
formally	The count was dressed *formally* in white tie and tails.
formerly	The preacher had *formerly* been an actor.
forth	Sir Kay went *forth* to battle.
fourth	Mrs. Summers was the *fourth* one to be invited.
its	The tree had lost *its* leaves.
it's (it is)	This time *it's* my turn to go first.
later	Do not return *later* than twelve o'clock.
latter	Of your four excuses I prefer the *latter*.
lead	The treasure map will *lead* you to the gold. The husband and wife now *lead* a happy life.
led	Evil companions *led* him astray.
loose	There is a *loose* board in the floor.
lose	If we *lose* another game, we *lose* the championship.
passed	The river *passed* by our home. The student was *passed* with a D.
past	History gives us a record of the *past*.

principal	Is Mr. Conklin a typical high school *principal?* His *principal* objection is the cost.
principle	He accepted the *principle* of nonsegregation.
prophecy (n)	Many people in 1843 believed Miller's *prophecy*.
prophesy (v)	Many *prophesy* that a third world war will bring total destruction.
quiet	Be *quiet;* the baby is asleep.
quite	Grandma is *quite* deaf.
respectfully	The letter closed: "Yours *respectfully*."
respectively	The scholarships were awarded to Andrew, Betty, and Grace, *respectively*.
right	I am *right* behind you. Joe injured his *right* hand.
rite	We loved the pageantry of the coronation *rite*.
write	Please *write* me a letter when you arrive home.
sight	The accident cost the miner the *sight* of one eye.
site	Here was the perfect *site* for the new store.
cite	When you quote, you must *cite* the source.
stationary	The sentry was *stationary* at his post.
stationery	Use some of your new *stationery* for the letter.
statue	Meet me by the *statue* of General Lee.
stature	His impressive stature made him tower over the others.
statute	Tom's conviction was based on an old *statute* passed by the legislature in 1831.
their	Politely, the boys tipped *their* hats.
there	She asked if *there* were any left.
they're	"*They're* off!" shouted Mazie as the starter's gun cracked.
to	Try *to* understand.
too	There is *too* much confusion.
two	*Two* of us, Ken and I, are planning trips.
weather	The *weather* continues rainy.
whether	We do not know *whether* or not we should take our trip.

whose	I wonder *whose* book this is.
who's	"*Who's* your girl now, Henry," teased Frank.
your	Don't tell me *your* pen is leaking!
you're	Don't tell me *you're* going to Seattle again!

Exercises for

1. CORRECT WORD CHOICE

Directions: In the blank space before each sentence write the number that stands for the correct word.

_____ 1. His release from the army was (1 affected 2 effected) by the senator.

_____ 2. (1 It's 2 Its) one of the best paintings he has produced.

_____ 3. We object in (1 principal 2 principle) to such unfounded charges.

_____ 4. The announcer had (1 formally 2 formerly) been a heavy-weight wrestler.

_____ 5. "Run," shouted the coed. "It's (1 later 2 latter) than you think."

_____ 6. The fife and drum (1 corpse 2 corps) furnished music for the parade.

_____ 7. You must remain (1 quite 2 quiet) while the child is reciting.

_____ 8. The men saluted sharply as the flag (1 passed 2 past) by.

_____ 9. "What do I have to (1 loose 2 lose)?" she said, shrugging her shoulders.

_____ 10. She (1 lead 2 led) him a dog's life.

_____ 11. The headmaster admitted that they had tried to do (1 there 2 they're 3 their) best.

_____ 12. The voters objected to his (1 affected 2 effected) mannerisms.

_____ 13. The editor fought a (1 dual 2 duel) with the rival editor.

_____ 14. Now that the family is (1 altogether 2 all together), we must have an old-fashioned taffy pull.

_____ 15. I must ask you to (1 accept 2 except) my resignation.

_____ 16. How could anyone (1 device 2 devise) such a plan?

_____ 17. More and more (1 statues 2 statures 3 statutes) are being written into the law books each year.

_____ 18. Scholars debated the question of how many (1 angels 2 angles) could stand on the point of a pin.

_____ 19. No one can go (1 accept 2 except) Charles.

Exercises for

2. CORRECT WORD CHOICE

Directions: In the blank space before each sentence write the number that stands for the correct word.

_____ 1. The old prospector was lost on the (1 desert 2 dessert).

_____ 2. Everyone was there (1 accept 2 except) Mr. Ligon.

_____ 3. Let me tell you that (1 your 2 you're) wrong about him.

_____ 4. (1 It's 2 Its) paw was caught in the steel trap.

_____ 5. The (1 principal 2 principle) announced the new appointments to the teaching staff.

_____ 6. My uncle gave me good (1 council 2 counsel 3 consul) about leaving school.

_____ 7. ("1 Who's 2 Whose) car are you driving?" I asked.

_____ 8. No one can (1 prophecy 2 prophesy) with certainty what may happen in the East.

_____ 9. I do not think he will (1 loose 2 lose) by trading in his old car.

_____ 10. The old man was formerly a guide employed at the (1 capital 2 capitol).

_____ 11. We found, to our sorrow, that they had (1 all ready 2 already) gone.

_____ 12. The old miner brushed his hands through his (1 coarse 2 course) hair.

_____ 13. The mechanic found that a nut had come (1 loose 2 lose).

_____ 14. The group of businessmen started the bank with less than a million dollars in (1 capital 2 capitol).

_____ 15. The clown stood (1 stationery 2 stationary) on his hands.

_____ 16. The committee (1 respectively 2 respectfully) submitted its annual report.

_____ 17. Herb told me that (1 your 2 you're) going to the beach over the Fourth.

_____ 18. All the members of the staff (1 accepted 2 excepted) our invitation.

_____ 19. The people living on Grant Street presented their petition to the (1 council 2 counsel 3 consul).

Don'ts

1. *Don't permit modifiers to dangle.*

> Wrong: Having worked all day, the floor was finally finished.
>
> Right: Having worked all day, the carpenter finally finished the floor.

> Wrong: After trying on a number of hats, the saleslady finally sold Mrs. Lawrence a blue straw.
>
> Right: After trying on a number of hats, Mrs. Lawrence finally purchased a blue straw.

> Wrong: Several samples of material had been sent, thus giving the customer a good choice.
>
> Right: Since the customer should have a good choice, several samples of material had been sent.

> Wrong: On opening the can, the peaches were found to be spoiled.
>
> Right: On opening the can, we found the peaches to be spoiled.

> Wrong: To understand these directions, the label must be studied carefully.
>
> Right: To understand these directions, one must study the label carefully.

> Wrong: While trying on a new pair of sandals in the store, a fire truck roared by.
>
> Right: While I was trying on a new pair of sandals in the store, a fire truck roared by.

> Wrong: When six years old, his father retired to a farm near Medford.
>
> Right: When Walter was six years old, his father retired to a farm near Medford.

2. *Don't fail to express parallel ideas in parallel grammatical form.*

Wrong: Walt said that he liked hiking into hills and to go fishing.

Right: Walt said that he liked to go fishing and to hike into hills.

Wrong: You are either going to pay this bill, or I am going to sue you.

Right: Either you are going to pay this bill, or I am going to sue you.

Wrong: On our trip to Yellowstone Park we met Mike Wilson, a typical cowboy, and who had lived in Wyoming all his life.

Right: On our trip to Yellowstone Park we met Mike Wilson, a typical cowboy who had lived in Wyoming all his life.

Wrong: She was not only confused by the road signs, but she had left her glasses at home.

Right: Not only was she confused by the road signs, but she had left her glasses at home.

Wrong: On my trip I visited both with Leonard and Edward.

Right: On my trip I visited both with Leonard and with Edward.
        On my trip I visited with both Leonard and Edward.

3. *Don't use an adjective where you should use an adverb, or an adverb where you should use an adjective.*

Wrong: Marie sings *good.*
Right: Marie sings *well.*

Wrong: I am *sure* happy about your good fortune.
Right: I am *surely* happy about your good fortune.

Wrong: You must visit us again *real* soon.
Right: You must visit us again *very* soon.

Wrong: The flowers in the hanging baskets smell *sweetly.*
Right: The flowers in the hanging baskets smell *sweet.*

Wrong: Everyone felt *badly* about his accident.
Right: Everyone felt *bad* about his accident.

Wrong: *Most* everyone felt that he had been mistreated.

Right: *Almost* everyone felt that he had been mistreated.

4. *Don't needlessly separate related parts of a sentence and don't misplace modifiers.*

Wrong: The merchant adds all receipts taken in each day *on an adding machine.*

Right: *On an adding machine* the merchant adds all receipts taken in each day.

Wrong: I *only* want one sandwich for lunch.

Right: I want *only* one sandwich for lunch.

Wrong: Everyone has *not* turned in his assignment.

Right: *Not* everyone has turned in his assignment.

Wrong: I have some candy *in my desk* that Bertie made.

Right: *In my desk* I have some candy that Bertie made.

Wrong: We tried to *immediately and completely* remove all evidence.

Right: We tried to remove all evidence *completely and immediately.*

Exercises for

1. DON'TS

Directions: In the blank space before each sentence write the number that stands for the error. If no error is present, leave the space blank.

1. Dangling modifier
2. Faulty parallel structure

3. Adjective and adverb confused
4. Misplaced modifier

_____ 1. Only the other day a woman was arrested by our local sheriff in a state of extreme intoxication.

_____ 2. While sitting on the steps in front of the library, a new red convertible drove up and honked twice.

_____ 3. Jimmie sat down at the counter and ordered a cup of coffee with a grin.

_____ 4. My vacation being over, everyone expected me to begin work with renewed energy.

_____ 5. You look beautifully in that new dress, Miss Jones.

_____ 6. Turning suddenly off the main road, the large white house came into view.

_____ 7. The purpose of these gatherings is to find a fair method of sharing the responsibility.

_____ 8. Most all of the city was destroyed by fire at that time.

_____ 9. Nearly everyone I know likes to walk about the paths and looking at the flowers and trees.

_____ 10. I don't think that he will finish this puzzle very quick.

_____ 11. Leaning against the wall and looking out over the bay, a small sloop could be seen beating to windward.

_____ 12. Looking hopefully at the student, the teacher awaited his answer through her bifocals.

_____ 13. After breaking the seals and entering the musty tomb, the excavators found the body of the emperor.

_____ 14. There is nothing like getting up early, taking a brisk walk, and to come home to a good breakfast of hot cakes, bacon, eggs, and coffee.

_____ 15. While eating meals, his habit of snapping his fingers annoyed everyone at the table.

Exercises for

2. DON'TS

Directions: In the blank space before each sentence write the number that stands for the error. If no error is present, leave the space blank.

1. Dangling modifier
2. Faulty parallel structure
3. Adjective and adverb confused
4. Misplaced modifier

_____ 1. Covered with stains and spotted with finger marks, my copy of this book brought very little at the auction.

_____ 2. Andrews was not only courteous to all the guests, but to the employees as well.

_____ 3. Everyone was not pleased at his display of egotism.

_____ 4. Without trying again, how can you be sure that you will fail?

_____ 5. Before making a reply, your answer should be carefully considered.

_____ 6. Isn't this a real pleasant day today, Mrs. Jameson?

_____ 7. Without having asked for specific approval, he took the affair into his own hands and made the proper decision.

_____ 8. Written in words of one syllable, any child can understand this story.

_____ 9. We quickly gathered that our neighbors were out of town because their shades were drawn, their lawn had not been cut, and several papers were strewn about the front porch.

_____ 10. The jumping tactics were used to shake off parasites, to catch flies, and in escaping from enemies.

_____ 11. To be a star performer, hours and hours of practice are necessary.

_____ 12. I not only found it necessary to examine all the books in our library; but also all those in the city library.

_____ 13. The students thronged down the street, waving their lighted torches in time to the song that they were shouting.

_____ 14. My friend had a very expensive movie camera in Europe that was lost.

Exercises for

3. DON'TS

Directions: In the blank space before each sentence write the number that stands for the error. If no error is present, leave the space blank.

1. Dangling modifier
2. Faulty parallel structure
3. Adjective and adverb confused
4. Misplaced modifier

_____ 1. He certainly sang that song as good as any professional could.

_____ 2. He was not only an expert in physics but also in chemistry.

_____ 3. Poorly clad, her request received little attention from the desk clerk.

_____ 4. The flowers in the window boxes smell fragrantly.

_____ 5. On entering the room, the officers found their man huddling in an armchair, his head sunk in apathy.

_____ 6. Many women and children were employed during the war in our place of business.

_____ 7. Having spent all his money, James's father refused to send him any more.

_____ 8. About half of the seats were filled by students that had no backs.

_____ 9. The evidence looks badly for your client.

_____ 10. Long practice having given the brothers unusual dexterity, they were able to do more work in one day than any other two men.

_____ 11. Your house on the lake is real picturesque.

_____ 12. When visiting such places after dark, a flashlight is almost a necessity.

_____ 13. The scholar is supposed to cheer, to inspire, and sometimes guiding men where they should go.

_____ 14. We crossed the Atlantic on a jet liner operated by an English firm over one hundred feet long.

_____ 15. Not only was he pleased with my efforts, but he insisted that I supply him with additional paintings.

_____ 16. To be able to translate this passage clearly, a good dictionary would help.

_____ 17. Your sister sings sweetly and with good expression.

89

Test One

PART I. SENTENCE COMPLETENESS

<u>Directions:</u> In the blank space before each of the following write:

1. if the group of words would not ordinarily be punctuated as a complete sentence (sentence fragment);
2. if the group of words is a single complete sentence;
3. if the group of words as it stands constitutes more than would be punctuated as one complete sentence (comma fault or run-together sentence).

__2__ 1. To this new country came Daniel Gookin with his wife and son.

__1__ 2. An intellectual and artistic revival, flowering in fourteenth-century Italy and developing and ripening later in Germany, France, and Italy.

__3__ 3. God had struck at New England, if its colonists did not reform they would be ruined.

__1__ 4. As a sceptic and rationalist who took pleasure in exposing the errors of those whom he considered slaves of emotion.

__2__ 5. There were a number of stories about the Indian wars, some of them bare chronicles, some more elaborate.

__3__ 6. His sermons were marvelous indeed they were too marvelous for historians to go on swallowing in an age of increasing rationalism.

__1__ 7. Buried at midnight by Stella's side in St. Patrick's Church under the epitaph "Where savage indignation can tear the heart no more."

__1__ 8. One pleasant but stupid, the other unpleasant but wise.

91

__2__ 9. What mutually attracted Addison and Steele is hard to say.

__3__ 10. Burns was not a besotted drunkard he probably drank no more than most of his contemporaries.

__2__ 11. New friends crowding to his rescue, he was able to continue the work that he had begun years before.

a

__3__ 12. There is a minimum of red tape, in fact, everything possible is done to make the trip pleasant.

__3__ 13. This room was the kindergarten, it had been cleared, and the painted walls showed clean squares.

PART II. SENTENCE CORRECTNESS

Directions: Some of the following sentences contain errors in agreement, case, reference, verb forms, spelling, modifiers, parallel structure, and adjective or adverb. If any sentence is incorrect, draw a circle around the number that represents the sentence containing the error. You may have any number of wrong sentences from none to five. You may assume that the punctuation is correct.

1 ②3 4 5   1. 1 An increase in your wages, together with more responsibilities, are proposed. 2 There is a number of considerations that Congress should take up. 3 The book of directions tells you exactly how to assemble the machine. 4 Every man has a right to his own thoughts. 5 Alice is the girl who I told you about.

1 2 3 4 5   2. 1 The lady invited both of us—Henry and me —to breakfast. 2 On the floor stand three huge pottery dogs. 3 Natives told us about his coming to visit them. 4 Neither you nor he has any right to judge. 5 His principle trouble was financial.

①2 ③④5   3. 1 Us girls had given up hope. 2 Someone has left his books on the desk. 3 We found that our water pipes had froze. 4 Andrew, together with his mother, is to visit us. 5 The manager feels certain that it was he who stole the camera.

1 2 ③4⑤   4. 1 It's too late to remedy your error. 2 He doesn't know why you have come. 3 The maid felt bad about her accident. 4 Both the staff and the manager are eager to please.

93

5 For sale: Television set by a gentleman with a 21-inch screen.

1 ②3 4 ⑤   5.   1 You may depend upon his misunderstanding your directions. 2 It was he whom I meant. 3 Raising my hat, I continued to stare at Ruth and her. 4 As each girl entered, the attendant gave them a basket. 5 While in the city of San Francisco, the fog obscured the Golden Gate Bridge.

1 2 3 ④ 5   6.   1 What do you think of a man who says that? 2 Is it too dark for you to see the road? 3 There seem to be many errors in this paper. 4 This is one of the most beautiful statues that exist. 5 A large number of horses has been shipped from the range.

1 2 3 ④ 5   7.   1 Dave and he had all ready gone. 2 There are several reasons why you should go. 3 The President, together with the members of his cabinet, were invited. 4 Who could sing this song better than her? 5 The monkeys and the elephant were being fed.

①②3 ④⑤   8.   1 "I want each of you to do their best," urged the instructor. 2 Between you and I, I think him jealous. 3 James was a little under six feet in stature. 4 Tom took out his key, entered his car, and put it in his pocket. 5 Mrs. Murphy is one of those women who has trouble making chowder.

①②③ 4 ⑤   9.   1 Give this ticket to whoever he sends. 2 An index to the volumes were prepared. 3 No one is eligible unless he has passed twelve hours. 4 Nearly everyone has given his consent. 5 Jane is younger by three years than me.

1②③④5   10.   1 I will tell you who is responsible. 2 John Milton wrote one of the greatest epics that have ever been written. 3 I only have a few minutes before my train leaves. 4 Neither the students nor the teacher has heard a thing. 5 Go with him and me to see the monkeys.

1 2 3④5   11.   1 Whom have you sent? 2 You have forgotten me, I think. 3 No one but him was present. 4 I had rode down the trail that morning. 5 It's later than you think.

①2 3 4 5   12.   1 I put the magazine in the box that I had read. 2 I saw him coming down the street with Jane and her. 3 Both of us—Harvey and me—had seen him. 4 Every boy and girl must develop their personality. 5 Suzy had written me only a postcard.

1 2③④5   13.   1 I like to eat at Lawry's. They serve such good prime ribs. 2 When studying a new assignment, an outline should be made. 3 Of coarse, we could be wrong. 4 The owner gave Virgil and I a season's pass. 5 Children were forbidden to go into the tower of the capitol.

1②3 4⑤   14.   1 The bird sang sweetly in the bush. 2 When I come home, my dog barked happily. 3 Running across the street, my feet slipped. 4 Joe laid down under the tree and fell asleep. 5 Everyone should do their best.

①②3 4⑤   15.   1 Tell whoever comes that I may be late. 2 The odious and ridiculous parts of their character lies on the surface. 3 Take whomever you wish. 4 None of the men will take his share of responsibility. 5 Aunt Bessie gave watches to three of us—my two sisters and I.

1②3 4⑤   16.   1 Mother gave Jimmy and me the list, but we forgot it. 2 My hope that you have profited from the words of wisdom I have read you are sincere. 3 Both of us were grateful to the man. 4 Neither of these suggestions have been proposed before. 5 One should put himself in the place of the characters if they wish to enjoy this book.

①②③④⑤ 17. 1 Everyone in the party was required to use
                their power to advance the cause. 2 Neither
                Jimmy nor his friends are able to do good
                work under these conditions. 3 The dog
                team begun their arduous journey. 4 The
                knight in shiny armor had slain the dragon.
                5 In large drafting rooms one or more check-
                ers is employed.

1②③④⑤ 18. 1 Could it have been he who moved the
                chair? 2 The first snow of the winter come
                last week. 3 She don't speak very clearly.
                4 I only have a dollar bill in my wallet.
                5 Has anybody a question they wish an-
                swered?

PART III. PUNCTUATION

Directions: Supply punctuation wherever needed. Then in the blanks before each sentence write in order the letters that represent the punctuation you have supplied. Write _e_ if no mark of punctuation is needed.

a. comma
b. semicolon
c. quotation marks
d. apostrophe in preceding word

e. no punctuation or capitalization needed
f. capital letter
g. hyphen

_g e f e_   1. Hers is probably the finest one–woman show₂ that has been seen in the northwest this ₄summer.

_a a a e_   2. The trouble₁ I think₂ is not serious₃ but you should make every effort to see₄ that it is not repeated.

_a a e e_   3. Their Siamese cat₁ which was named Dingbat₂ gave a yowl₃ and sprang away from the man₄ who had stepped on her tail.

_e e a a_   4. After glancing quickly ₁east and then ₂west, Mrs. Ragan brushed past him₃ darted inside₄ grabbed my sleeve, and told me to be quiet.

_a a a a_   5. They liked the empty theater₁ the set₂ the lighting₃ the producers₄ jokes, and the actors.

_a d a c_   6. "I think we have done all that can be done," he answered₁ "its₂ a queer case₃ though, and I knew your taste for such things.₄"

_d a a e_   7. "You're₁ wrong₂ Miss Green," said the usher₃ "I never said you could sit in the seats on the ₄north side."

_e e a d_   8. Although Mrs. Snow₁ and Mr. Carew overshadow the rest of the highly ₂ competent cast₃ Miss Ward, as the heros₄ sister is also effective.

_a a e a_   9. The words ₁"renaissance" and ₂"reformation" are convenient symbols for states of mind active in England and elsewhere in the seventeenth ₃ century₄ neither word is easy to define.

97

PART IV. SPELLING

Directions: In the space at the left write the number that corresponds to any misspelled word. If no word is misspelled, leave the space blank. No more than one misspelled word appears in any one line.

1. 1 concensus   2 tragedy   3 shriek   4 omitted

2. 1 preference   2 ghost   3 conferred   4 Wednesday

3. 1 supersede   2 picnic   3 occurred   4 bureau

4. 1 embarrass   2 believe   3 physical   4 instance

5. 1 primitive   2 accidentally   3 desperate   4 sylli-ble

6. 1 villian   2 mortgage   3 dilemma   4 aisle

7. 1 pertinent   2 incompatible   3 miniature   4 sand-witch

8. 1 thorough   2 concede   3 barbarious   4 preparatory

9. 1 arguing   2 clothes   3 ridiculous   4 equipement

10. 1 disastrous   2 lacquer   3 descendent   4 pastime

11. 1 writting   2 susceptible   3 harass   4 specimen

12. 1 calendar   2 acommodate   3 exhilarate   4 siege

13. 1 leisure   2 incredulous   3 hindrance   4 noticable

14. 1 occasion   2 conqueror   3 bacheler   4 pendulum

15. 1 receipt   2 psychology   3 dissipate   4 fragile

16. 1 changeable   2 apology   3 indescribable   4 prefferred

17. 1 wiry   2 temperature   3 humorous   4 succeed

18. 1 pyramid   2 lible   3 cemetery   4 innocence

19. 1 fundamental   2 politician   3 mermur   4 laboratory

20. 1 grievous   2 dealt   3 apparatus   4 until

21. 1 separate   2 receive   3 lieing   4 financier

22. 1 heir   2 battalion   3 inadvisable   4 village

23. 1 professor   2 disease   3 foreign   4 Britian

24. 1 Tuesday   2 absence   3 maneuver   4 persuade

25. 1 dependence   2 analize   3 inevitable   4 schedule

Test Two

PART I. SENTENCE COMPLETENESS

Directions: In the blank space before each of the following write:

1. if the group of words would not ordinarily be punctuated as a complete sentence (sentence fragment);

2. if the group of words is a single complete sentence;

3. if the group of words as it stands constitutes more than would be punctuated as one complete sentence (comma fault or run-together sentence).

_____ 1. She looked for a long time into Ann's face she did not say a word about the broken doll.

_____ 2. A quiet, sweet, gentle little woman who was obviously someone's grandmother.

_____ 3. It was a little after two o'clock when we drove up to the hotel.

_____ 4. This was what all the world was fighting about, he reflected, this was what the struggle was about.

_____ 5. A woman sat there fishing.

_____ 6. That everything was as it should be.

_____ 7. Outside, the snow was whirling fiercely, inside, the air was warm and faintly scented with the smell of fir.

_____ 8. A place where tired-looking businessmen could relax.

_____ 9. Had he not sat there night after night waiting to be called?

_____ 10. "We would charge you very little," she said, "Norris decides about the prices."

_____ 11. A ruined building extending over the water.

_____ 12. This, he told himself, is incredible.

_____ 13. The little dark-haired girl was one of the last who
          fell asleep, she had been crying for hours over the
          loss of the dog.

_____ 14. Mrs. Thompson laughed dutifully, but she did not
          think the joke funny.

_____ 15. It's never too late to make new resolutions, any
          bad habit can be broken.

PART II.   SENTENCE CORRECTNESS

Directions: Some of the following sentences contain errors in agreement, case, reference, verb forms, spelling, modifiers, parallel structure, and adjective or adverb. If any sentence is incorrect, draw a circle around the number that represents the sentence containing the error. You may have any number of wrong sentences from none to five. You may assume that the punctuation is correct.

1 2 3 4 5   1.   1 Shakespeare is one of the greatest dramatists who have ever lived.   2 You sure do walk fast.   3 Looking quickly at his companion, Harry dived into the pool.   4 The cream tasted sour to Helen.   5 Each of his fingers was badly frozen.

1 2 3 4 5   2.   1 Everyone seemed pleased with their progress in the course.   2 The counsel met in the City Hall on Monday.   3 My sister is older than me.   4 Jim was born in a log cabin in the mountains that his grandfather built.   5 I have no fear of his not succeeding in his work.

1 2 3 4 5   3.   1 Each student must have his photograph taken.   2 Some real effective new weapons have been invented.   3 On the picnic everyone waited on themselves.   4 Who do you think he is?   5 Everyone who wishes to succeed must do their best.

1 2 3 4 5   4.   1 Who knows better than her?   2 The duty fell to the three of us, Tom, Walt, and me.   3 He paid his partner a compliment.   4 The book was laying under the desk.   5 A book or magazine give him no pleasure.

1 2 3 4 5   5.   1 The villain has drunk the poison he intended for the hero.   2 Rain and snow is allowed to beat upon the exposed material.   3 Every person is eligible if they send in an entry blank.   4 The curtain is not to raise before eight o'clock.   5 When only a baby, our old home was sold.

1 2 3 4 5   6.   1 Everyone should do their best to fight inflation.   2 Are you as happy as she?   3 This

is one of the books that interest me. 4 You
may deliver the message to whoever comes
to the door. 5 The usefulness of these
methods and principles vary a great deal.

1 2 3 4 5   7. 1 How long has your dog laid in that position? 2 We girls—Joan, Sue, and I—sat
quietly. 3 Public speaking helps a person
because it gives them assurance. 4 Either
Marian or I will go with you. 5 The boy
sat the plate on the shelf and sighed softly.

1 2 3 4 5   8. 1 This devise is guaranteed to open cans.
2 Neither William nor his friends were at
the door. 3 They appointed you and I on
the committee. 4 Who do you suppose will
win? 5 When a youth is caught speeding,
they must be punished.

1 2 3 4 5   9. 1 There is the possibility that it might have
been he. 2 The principal and interest are
safeguarded. 3 A disaster of such propor-
tions is a national calamity. 4 Laziness and
stupidity is his chief weakness. 5 Every
man, woman, and child is encouraged to
save.

1 2 3 4 5   10. 1 I felt bad about my error. 2 I accept your
apology gladly. 3 Each of the volumes was
carefully replaced. 4 The girl in red might
have been she. 5 Al had broke his wrist
once before.

1 2 3 4 5   11. 1 No one should admit that he was not
present on time. 2 Who do you think I look
like? 3 Announce this to whoever comes to
the office. 4 The sandwiches and coffee is
ready. 5 We can give aid to whoever
needs it.

1 2 3 4 5   12. 1 Neither the players nor the coach is likely
to complain. 2 I accept your offer of a posi-
tion. 3 Every man, woman, and child meet
the same difficulty. 4 We were puzzled
about him taking his vacation in February.
5 Gloria felt badly about the burned cake.

1 2 3 4 5   13. 1 She lay down an hour ago to take her nap.
2 I do not know whom to trust. 3 The duel

was fought in the early morning. 4 That is a spot around which clusters many beautiful memories. 5 The weak part of his team were his pitchers.

1 2 3 4 5 14. 1 I find him altogether too blunt. 2 Aunt Mary asked Scott and me to visit her. 3 Each of the countries that have state railroads was visited by the commission. 4 Jim and his two dogs have just returned home. 5 Who shall go, she or I?

1 2 3 4 5 15. 1 We never would have expected the visitors to be them. 2 Each of them think they know all the answers. 3 Irwin's stand was a matter of principal. 4 The rapidity of the advances have created a problem of supply. 5 Give these reports to whoever the registrar sends.

1 2 3 4 5 16. 1 Everyone felt badly about the loss of the game. 2 The man who they believed innocent was finally freed. 3 I like to fish, to play golf, and hiking also. 4 Each child has his own set of crayons. 5 Has everybody given you his name?

1 2 3 4 5 17. 1 There is too many people in this group. 2 Everyone is not likely to make a million dollars. 3 My uncle, together with my Aunt Lizzie, is planning to visit us. 4 The gardener asks us to carefully and promptly plant the roses. 5 She was stabbed with one of the steak knives that is kept in a drawer here in the dining room.

1 2 3 4 5 18. 1 She was not only beautiful but intelligent. 2 Neither of these applicants write a good letter. 3 Can you imagine him doing the ballet! 4 The waiter was dressed formally. 5 Whose coming?

PART III.   PUNCTUATION

Directions: Supply punctuation wherever needed. Then in the blanks before each sentence write in order the letters that represent the punctuation you have supplied. Write *e* if no mark of punctuation is needed.

a. comma
b. semicolon
c. quotation marks
d. apostrophe in preceding word

e. no punctuation or capitalization needed
f. capital letter
g. hyphen

————— 1. "She was the daughter of a carpenter in Randolph₁ Massachusetts"₂ said ₃professor Quinn, "but₄ as a child she lived in Vermont."

————— 2. The play was presented at the Chestnut Street₁ theater on January 8, 1830₂ it proved to be Smiths₃ best three ₄ act play.

————— 3. "I did it at once₁ sir,₂ said Gregson. "I have had advertisements sent to all the newspapers₃ and one of my men has gone to the American Exchange, but he hasnt₄ returned yet."

————— 4. As the whirl of dust drew nearer to the solitary bluff upon which the two castaways were reposing₁ the canvas ₂ covered wagons and the figures of armed horsemen began to show up through the haze₃ and the apparition revealed itself as being a great caravan upon its journey for the ₄west.

————— 5. "Yes₁ maam,"₂ I said. "Its₃ a childrens₄ game the way your husband plays it."

————— 6. Well₁ we visited for a week in Elgin₂ Illinois₃ then we spent a week with my relatives in Canton₄ Missouri.

————— 7. The old maple₁ which stood at the ₂southwest corner of the house₃ had finally been removed,₄ it left a gap that seemed enormous.

————— 8. People wondered₁ how I could have been talked into spending my vacation in ₂east Africa₃ but I couldnt₄ tell them all the reasons.

PART IV. SPELLING

Directions: In the space at the left write the number that corresponds to any misspelled word. If no word is misspelled, leave the space blank. No more than one misspelled word appears in any one line.

_____ 1.   1 foremost   2 Tuesday   3 inoculate   4 delt

_____ 2.   1 preparatory   2 untill   3 forehead   4 lying

_____ 3.   1 accidentally   2 believe   3 grievous   4 susceptible

_____ 4.   1 laboratory   2 omitt   3 exceed   4 disastrous

_____ 5.   1 desperate   2 eighth   3 rheumatism   4 morgage

_____ 6.   1 picnicing   2 incredulous   3 ghost   4 similar

_____ 7.   1 conscience   2 accomodate   3 thorough   4 ridiculous

_____ 8.   1 parlament   2 occurred   3 humorous   4 feminine

_____ 9.   1 equipped   2 paralyze   3 apparatus   4 preferred

_____ 10.   1 supersede   2 receive   3 liesure   4 dissipate

_____ 11.   1 illegible   2 hoping   3 bureau   4 argueing

_____ 12.   1 optimistic   2 noticeable   3 financeir   4 subtle

_____ 13.   1 maneuver   2 lightning   3 hypocrisy   4 fragile

_____ 14.   1 descendant   2 harrass   3 apology   4 partner

_____ 15.   1 strictly   2 primitive   3 exaggerate   4 battallion

_____ 16.   1 acknowlegment   2 persuade   3 villain   4 sensible

_____ 17.   1 foreign   2 incompatible   3 all right   4 clothes

_____ 18.   1 heir   2 physician   3 schedule   4 pyramid

_____ 19.   1 temperament   2 accumulate   3 incidentally   4 occurr

_____ 20.   1 superintendent   2 politician   3 minature   4 changeable

_____ 21.   1 aisle   2 apparent   3 dissappoint   4 siege

_____ 22.   1 occassion   2 fundamental   3 familiar   4 conferred

_____ 23.   1 guard   2 parallell   3 succeed   4 repetition

_____ 24.   1 lacquor   2 divine   3 courteous   4 benefited

_____ 25.   1 mischievous   2 specimen   3 parenthesis   4 calender

Test Three

PART I.   SENTENCE COMPLETENESS

Directions: In the blank space before each of the following write:

1.   if the group of words would not ordinarily be punctuated as a complete sentence (sentence fragment);

2.   if the group of words is a single complete sentence;

3.   if the group of words as it stands constitutes more than would be punctuated as one complete sentence (comma fault or run-together sentence).

_____   1.   The aftermath of the Revolution told in a stimulating new way through contemporary reports, letters, and court transcripts.

_____   2.   Troy's nature freshened within him, he thought he would rest and bathe here before going farther.

_____   3.   Taking care not to tread on the grass, we will go along the straight walk ̣to the west front.

_____   4.   An enthralling story of emotional conflict among a group of high-strung people isolated in a Swiss sanitorium.

_____   5.   Ernest, a German soldier on furlough from the Eastern front, wants to return to the quiet of his parents' house in a homeland that he pictures as unseared by war.

_____   6.   Our grandfather, fervently, appealingly, lyrically, delivered a long improvisation of prayer.

_____   7.   His black hair hung to his shoulders, and he also had a bristly mustache which did not conceal his brutal mouth, nor was there any beard to hide his broad, swarthy jowl.

_____   8.   It often gets hot like this down here even in the wintertime.

———— 9. He forgives Shakespeare many extravagances, Marlowe, Ford, Massinger, Beaumont and Fletcher, Middleton, Dekker none.

———— 10. Then the business manager told us that the orchestra and two-thirds of the first balcony had been sold out for the evening performance.

———— 11. Born on a large farm south of Junction City.

———— 12. The air is clean and sweet, fireflies wink along the river.

———— 13. One of the most talented pianists in Europe and one who plans to make a tour of this country next winter.

PART II. SENTENCE CORRECTNESS

Directions: Some of the following sentences contain errors in agreement, case, reference, verb forms, spelling, modifiers, parallel structure, and adjective or adverb. If any sentence is incorrect, draw a circle around the number that represents the sentence containing the error. You may have any number of wrong sentences from none to five. You may assume that the punctuation is correct.

1 2 3 4 5   1.   1 There was four left-handed pitchers on the Fresno team.   2 What are the chances of me leaving the office early?   3 The tramp said he wanted only a cup of coffee.   4 I found that Marvin had all ready gone.   5 Someone has left his coat on the chair.

1 2 3 4 5   2.   1 Whom have you selected for the office?   2 Peterson, as well as Moe, are all-Americans.   3 I dove into the pool and swum for the opposite side.   4 I except your invitation to dinner.   5 There is all together too much talking and not enough action.

1 2 3 4 5   3.   1 The best time for sleep is the hours from eleven to two.   2 If a person breaks a leg or otherwise injures themselves is the state responsible?   3 Every station attendant should do his best to be courteous.   4 Have you froze your fingers?   5 There were few negative votes cast.

1 2 3 4 5   4.   1 Every one of the drivers denies their responsibility.   2 Some one of the boys did his best to wreck the plan.   3 He laid his pen carefully on the table.   4 The sheriff tried to determine who the guilty ones were.   5 Who has he chosen to play the part of Charlie?

1 2 3 4 5   5.   1 Either Dorothy or her sisters are to blame.   2 Both my brother and my sister was sick.   3 Do you know weather he is here?   4 Each officer must perform their duties efficiently.   5 A plate of vegetables were on the table.

1 2 3 4 5   6.   1 The villain drank the poison I would have drunk.   2 My family, Father, Mother, and I, accept your thanks.   3 I feel badly about

your accident. 4 When he come to the river, he borrowed a boat. 5 The friends of the senator praised him highly.

1 2 3 4 5   7. 1 Every child should be encouraged to save their pennies. 2 When seven years old, my mother determined to send me to college. 3 Buy me some white stationery, please. 4 All was quite along the front. 5 "They're coming!" Mort shouted.

1 2 3 4 5   8. 1 Whoever used this machine last did not do their work well. 2 My father, together with my two uncles, were very fond of him. 3 I had seen the gun lying in the trench. 4 It was he, not they, who came in late. 5 Each of the contestants who entered a song was certain they had won.

1 2 3 4 5   9. 1 Do not loose your money, son. 2 Every one of the camp sites are carefully chosen. 3 From the mountains was heard the noise of thunder. 4 There was a pile of old clothes in the corner. 5 She lead a very unhappy life.

1 2 3 4 5   10. 1 The thief could never have been she. 2 It was them who called. 3 Sue is taller than me. 4 Father gave Gene and me new bicycles. 5 Rushing across the street, my shoes became covered with tar.

1 2 3 4 5   11. 1 Give the tickets to whoever comes. 2 A person should not give away his last cent. 3 She can swim as well as he. 4 Us boys have often wanted to visit him. 5 Who do you think will be next year's editor?

1 2 3 4 5   12. 1 Have you began your work yet? 2 His books have lain in the corner since yesterday. 3 The governor went with his wife and she to the reception. 4 Evan and me are planning to visit Boston. 5 Mr. Harvey spoke sharply to both of us, Walt and me.

1 2 3 4 5   13. 1 You done right in reporting that incident to the police. 2 If anyone thinks he can do better, let them try. 3 She set down and cried softly. 4 He was one of those men

who have to shave twice a day. 5 You, together with your friends, is invited.

1 2 3 4 5 14. 1 I consider her to be the wholesome type.
2 He told us that neither the captain nor the
mates were able to sail at once. 3 One of
her maidenly qualities were certainly mod-
esty. 4 He has done very good on the first
part of the test. 5 Two dogs were laying on
the floor.

1 2 3 4 5 15. 1 Mother gave Mary and I a cookie. 2 Could
it have been she whom you saw? 3 There
remain many problems to be discussed.
4 The necessity for such rapid decisions have
long been apparent. 5 I had wrote him
about the bad weather.

1 2 3 4 5 16. 1 William, as well as Mary, have expressed
an interest in the sale. 2 That is the house
around which centers many happy memories.
3 Each of the seeds were carefully planted.
4 To such noble characters belongs the
glory. 5 Neither the two mates nor the
captain was saved from the wreck.

1 2 3 4 5 17. 1 Whom do you think I resemble? 2 This is
one of the cases that intrigues me. 3 Here
are a packet of poems written by a sophomore. 4 It's too late for us to go with whoever comes. 5 Each of the poems are
accompanied by an illustration.

1 2 3 4 5 18. 1 Carter gave Louis and I a bit of good advice. 2 There is several reasons for his
choice. 3 I thought that the girl was she.
4 Every one of the men are catching fish.
5 On the table was lying two daggers.

PART III. PUNCTUATION

Directions: Supply punctuation wherever needed. Then in the blanks before each sentence write in order the letters that represent the punctuation you have supplied. Write *e* if no mark of punctuation is needed.

a. comma
b. semicolon
c. quotation marks
d. apostrophe in preceding word

e. no punctuation or capitalization needed
f. capital letter
g. hyphen

————— 1. "Do you know ₁professor Jones₂ who lives at 4364 Maple Drive?₃ asked Marjorie. "I am to call on him at eight o'clock.₄

————— 2. In his class in ₁history 201 Joe exhibited a remarkable knowledge of contemporary literature, ₂philosophy, and politics₃ didnt₄ he?

————— 3. "Why?₁ I asked in alarm. "Do you think shes₂ worse₃ Miss Bryan?₄

————— 4. Turning around to look him full in the face₁ Miss Thomas asked₂ "Major₃ why do you feel that the ₄west has been treated unfairly?"

————— 5. It was a comedy of errors₁ backs fumbled the ball₂ receivers₃ dropped passes₄ blockers missed their assignments.

————— 6. Dates, however₁ seem rather unimportant in Persian art₂ for its₃ course has been a coherent₄ and continuous one.

————— 7. Williamson, an ₁easterner, was a quiet₂ reserved man₃ however his employer₄ I am sorry to say, was far otherwise.

————— 8. Astonished₁ he looked at the door of his house₂ which stood open₃ he could not recall having opened it₄ nor could he recall how he came to be standing outside in the cold.

————— 9. "Any man₁ who spends that much money₂ should have a rich father," said Mrs. Jones₃ nodding her head at her youngest daughter₄ who sat demurely by the fire.

PART IV. SPELLING

Directions: In the space at the left write the number that corresponds to any misspelled word. If no word is misspelled, leave the space blank. No more than one misspelled word appears in any one line.

_____ 1. 1 grievous 2 indescribable 3 prairie 4 yacht

_____ 2. 1 useage 2 sophomore 3 seize 4 concede

_____ 3. 1 rhythm 2 committee 3 akward 4 dilemma

_____ 4. 1 hindrance 2 platow 3 recede 4 dependence

_____ 5. 1 across 2 height 3 conscience 4 firey

_____ 6. 1 acquainted 2 Tuesday 3 sandwich 4 pendulum

_____ 7. 1 instanse 2 parallel 3 disappear 4 until

_____ 8. 1 paralize 2 surprise 3 usually 4 tragedy

_____ 9. 1 hypnotize 2 picnic 3 Negroes 4 murmur

_____ 10. 1 ghost 2 weird 3 village 4 villian

_____ 11. 1 omit 2 preform 3 receipt 4 misspelled

_____ 12. 1 partner 2 ridiculous 3 humorus 4 preference

_____ 13. 1 innocense 2 aisle 3 pertinent 4 Massachusetts

_____ 14. 1 disease 2 conferred 3 dormatories 4 sincerely

_____ 15. 1 temperature 2 quizzes 3 primitive 4 psychology

_____ 16. 1 negligible 2 lonliness 3 burglar 4 forehead

_____ 17. 1 thorough 2 susceptible 3 subtle 4 believe

_____ 18. 1 hoping 2 calendar 3 phamplet 4 mosquito

_____ 19. 1 morgage 2 physical 3 shriek 4 forcible

_____ 20. 1 maneuver 2 instant 3 heir 4 embarass

_____ 21. 1 mathematics 2 ghastly 3 equipment 4 ecstasy

_____ 22. 1 parlament 2 frantically 3 feminine 4 conquer

_____ 23. 1 governor 2 divine 3 exceed 4 disastrous

_____ 24. 1 supersede 2 reign 3 pursue 4 manafacturer

_____ 25. 1 sensible 2 consensus 3 rheumatism 4 pyramid

113

PART TWO

A BRIEF REVIEW OF ENGLISH GRAMMAR

An accurate knowledge of grammar is based upon the ability to select subjects and verbs. In simple sentences in which the subject comes first and tells who or what performs the action of the verb that follows, this is easy. It is also easy to select the verb if it names the action or links the subject with words that follow. Thus it is elementary to be able to pick the subject and verb in such a sentence as "The janitor washed the window." We are talking about the janitor; hence *janitor* is the subject. What did the janitor do? He washed; hence *washed* is the verb. Only slightly more difficult are the sentences containing a linking verb. These verbs do not express action, but merely link the subject to the word or words that follow. "She is tall," for example, shows a linking verb, the present tense third person singular of the verb *be*. Common linking verbs are *become, appear, remain, seem, feel, taste, sound,* and *smell.*

English verbs may be one, two, three, or four words. By means of auxiliary verbs placed before what were originally present infinitives and past participles, English verbs show a variety of aspects or tenses. These auxiliary verbs are *be, do, have, must, may* and *might, can* and *could, will* and *would, shall* and *should.* Practice making two, three, and four word verbs for the following: *ring, go, write, shout, lose, drink, spring, dive,* and *slay.* You will notice that words like *not, always, seldom,* etc., frequently separate the words of the verb. Remember that these are not part of the verb.

The normal English sentence has the subject coming before the verb, but in order to secure variety, flexibility, and interest in writing one may use a number of devices to vary what would otherwise be a childish and immature method of expressing thought. One such device is the expletive *there,* which serves to throw the real subject behind the verb. Compare the sentence "Eleven men are on the team" with the sentence "There are eleven men on the team." *Men* is the subject in each sentence. *There* is never the subject of a sentence unless it is used, as it is in the beginning of this sentence, where it means the word *there*. A second method of avoiding "subject-first" sentences is by beginning with a phrase. Prepositional phrases and verbal phrases will be discussed later, but notice that in the following sentences, the subject (the person, place, or thing we are talking about) does not come first. "In the afternoon *I* watched a ball game." "From her open study window *Barbara* could watch the hills." "Opening her big blue eyes, *she* looked at him coyly." "After eating four slices of pie, *Paul* felt less hungry." "To check attendance *he* used a small device carried in his hand." A third method is to begin with an adverbial clause. This will be discussed later. "When I first met him, *he* was very much alive." "Before the United States entered the fray, the *War* seemed very remote." A fourth method is very obvious—merely begin with an adjective or adverb. "The brave, honest, courageous *people* gave all they had." "Not nearly enough *time* is spent in recreation." A fifth method —the method of inversion—requires that the sentence be turned around before the subject and verb can be determined. Study the following examples. "Gladly then did *he* lay down his life." "Whom have *you* asked?" " 'Is that thunder I hear?' *he* asked." "Never before have *I* heard such a statement." A sixth type of sentence omits the subject entirely and begins with an emphatic verb. "Would that he were here." "Come and get it." "Let us get to work." In imperative statements similar to the last two sentences, *you* may be considered the understood subject. The final subject-verb relation we need to consider is the delayed subject after *it*. This will be discussed later. It is merely a sort of appositive in which the verbal phrase or the noun clause is anticipated by an *it* that begins the sentence. Examples are "It is true *that the book is very, very dull*." "It is good *for us to read worth-while books*." "It is hard work *putting out a crown fire*." In these sentences the true subjects are the noun clause *that the book is very, very dull*, the infinitive phrase *for us to read worth-while books*, and the gerund phrase *putting out crown fires*. The anticipatory *it*, like the expletive *there*, throws the real subject behind the verb.

Exercises for

1. SUBJECTS OF SENTENCES

Directions: In the blank space before each sentence write the index number of the word used as the subject. If no subject is expressed in the sentence, leave the space blank.

_____ 1. Six^1 old-fashioned^2 dresses^3 of^4 silk^5 or^6 satin^7 hung^8 in^9 the^{10} closet.^{11}

_____ 2. All^1 along^2 the^3 four-hundred-mile^4 trip^5 one^6 encounters^7 incomparable^8 scenery.^{9}

_____ 3. Give^1 my^2 regards^3 to^4 your^5 aunt.^{6}

_____ 4. It^1 doesn't^2 help^3 the^4 unemployment^5 problem,^{6} certainly.^{7}

_____ 5. Never^1 has^2 there^3 been^4 such^5 a^6 demand^7 for^8 new^9 cars.^{10}

_____ 6. Of^1 the^2 total^3 population^4 only^5 one-half^6 are^7 French.^{8}

_____ 7. Will^1 you^2 ask^3 us^4 to^5 visit^6 you^7 again^8 sometime?^{9}

_____ 8. For^1 his^2 last^3 afternoon,^{4} Joe^5 had^6 planned^7 to^8 sail^9 across^{10} the^{11} bay.^{12}

_____ 9. Exasperated,^{1} Betty^2 cried,^{3} "Your^4 remarks^5 are^6 utter^7 nonsense."^{8}

_____ 10. On^1 the^2 west^3 side^4 of^5 the^6 street^7 there^8 were^9 small,^{10} insignificant^{11} shops.^{12}

_____ 11. Tell^1 her^2 to^3 come^4 back^5 tomorrow^6 morning.^{7}

_____ 12. Few^1 of^2 the^3 bargains^4 are^5 really^6 bargains.^{7}

_____ 13. Outside,^{1} roared^2 a^3 mighty^4 gale.^{5}

_____ 14. When^1 I^2 am^3 grown,^{4} I^5 want^6 to^7 live^8 here^9 always.^{10}

_____ 15. Drowsily,^{1} Jane^2 listened^3 to^4 the^5 chattering^6 and^7 splashing^8 of^9 the^{10} children.^{11}

_____ 16. Don't^1 go^2 too^3 far^4 up^5 the^6 beach.^{7}

_____ 17. Let^1 us^2 all^3 go^4 to^5 the^6 zoo.^{7}

_____ 18. To^1 her^2 own^3 ears,^{4} her^5 voice^6 sounded^7 perplexed.^{8}

_____ 19. There^1 was^2 no^3 doubt^4 of^5 that.^{6}

_____ 20. Some^1 of^2 the^3 others^4 went^5 down^6 to^7 the^8 wharf.^{9}

Exercises for

2. SUBJECTS OF SENTENCES

Directions: In the blank space before each sentence write the index number of the word used as the subject. If no subject is expressed in the sentence, leave the space blank.

_____ 1. Has[1] he[2] any[3] money?[4]

_____ 2. Sharply[1] he[2] said,[3] "Do[4] not[5] file[6] those."[7]

_____ 3. The[1] three[2] of[3] them[4] were[5] waiting[6] on[7] the[8] stairs.[9]

_____ 4. Why[1] should[2] it[3] be[4] more[5] dangerous[6] here[7] than[8] in[9] Colorado?[10]

_____ 5. Please[1] don't[2] hurry.[3]

_____ 6. The[1] quiet[2] of[3] the[4] night[5] was[6] shattered[7] by[8] a[9] shrill[10] cry.[11]

_____ 7. Who[1] can[2] answer[3] this[4] question?[5]

_____ 8. Then,[1] old[2] Pete[3] came[4] shuffling[5] back[6] to[7] the[8] house.[9]

_____ 9. Where[1] has[2] this[3] fuss[4] got[5] us[6] in[7] the[8] past?[9]

_____ 10. What[1] can[2] you[3] tell[4] us[5] about[6] this[7] accident?[8]

_____ 11. There[1] is[2] naturally[3] some[4] criticism[5] of[6] this[7] policy[8] in[9] high[10] places.[11]

_____ 12. None[1] of[2] the[3] peaceful[4] strollers[5] had[6] any[7] idea[8] of[9] how[10] the[11] accident[12] had[13] occurred.[14]

_____ 13. To[1] the[2] victor[3] belong[4] the[5] spoils.[6]

_____ 14. Not[1] all[2] men[3] have[4] this[5] unusual[6] ability.[7]

_____ 15. Inquisitive[1] as[2] a[3] squirrel,[4] he[5] frightened[6] the[7] natives[8] badly.[9]

_____ 16. There[1] was[2] no[3] answer[4] to[5] his[6] shout.[7]

_____ 17. With[1] the[2] uncontrollable[3] habit[4] of[5] a[6] lifetime,[7] Joel[8] touched[9] his[10] hat.[11]

_____ 18. Most[1] of[2] his[3] observations[4] were[5] addressed[6] to[7] his[8] father.[9]

_____ 19. Across[1] the[2] green[3] lawn[4] tripped[5] a[6] lovely[7] girl.[8]

_____ 20. Stop[1] talking[2] and[3] eat[4] your[5] fish.[6]

Exercises for

3. VERBS OF SENTENCES

Directions: In the blank space before each sentence write in order the index numbers of the word or words used as the verb.

_____ 1. Give[1] me[2] your[3] hand,[4] my[5] friend.[6]

_____ 2. Sam Hill[1] is[2] a[3] never-to-be-forgotten[4] hero.[5]

_____ 3. I[1] am[2] being[3] brave,[4] Mother.[5]

_____ 4. There[1] have[2] been[3] mistakes[4] made[5] on[6] scoring.[7]

_____ 5. Henry[1] might[2] have[3] been[4] hurt[5] on[6] the[7] second[8] play.[9]

_____ 6. What[1] can[2] an[3] old[4] man[5] do?[6]

_____ 7. Henry[1] had[2] never[3] been[4] lost[5] in[6] the[7] jungle.[8]

_____ 8. Are[1] you[2] interested[3] in[4] dogs?[5]

_____ 9. Police[1] are[2] fighting[3] the[4] vicious[5] racket.[6]

_____ 10. I[1] have[2] seldom[3] seen[4] a[5] more[6] courageous[7] act.[8]

_____ 11. Are[1] you[2] a[3] very[4] patient[5] man?[6]

_____ 12. Ask[1] me[2] more[3] questions.[4]

_____ 13. We[1] are[2] being[3] taken[4] for[5] a[6] ride[7] tomorrow.[8]

_____ 14. The[1] plan[2] had[3] never[4] been[5] completely[6] abandoned.[7]

_____ 15. I[1] am[2] very[3] glad[4] to[5] see[6] you.[7]

_____ 16. Have[1] you[2] ever[3] been[4] in[5] Italy?[6]

_____ 17. We[1] are[2] confident.[3]

_____ 18. You[1] will[2] be[3] pleased[4] to[5] learn[6] about[7] its[8] low[9] cost.[10]

_____ 19. You[1] may[2] occasionally[3] have[4] been[5] deceived[6] by[7] his[8] manner.[9]

_____ 20. Shall[1] I[2] see[3] you[4] there?[5]

4. VERBS OF SENTENCES

Directions: In the blank space before each sentence write in order the index number of the word or words used as the verb.

_____ 1. A^1 week^2 had^3 elapsed.^{4}

_____ 2. Her^1 husband^2 had^3 on^4 a^5 dark^6 blue^7 suit.^{8}

_____ 3. I^1 have^2 been^3 running.^{4}

_____ 4. They^1 greeted^2 me^3 cordially.^{4}

_____ 5. The^1 story^2 might^3 have^4 been^5 told^6 better.^{7}

_____ 6. She^1 was^2 coming^3 to^4 my^5 house.^{6}

_____ 7. I^1 gave^2 her^3 my^4 address.^{5}

_____ 8. How^1 can^2 you^3 say^4 such^5 things?^{6}

_____ 9. The^1 engine^2 had^3 been^4 used^5 in^6 a^7 lumber^8 camp.^{9}

_____ 10. We^1 were^2 hot^3 and^4 dusty.^{5}

_____ 11. I^1 might^2 have^3 been^4 thrown^5 from^6 the^7 horse.^{8}

_____ 12. Tom^1 replaced^2 the^3 worn^4 needle.^{5}

_____ 13. The^1 animal^2 appeared^3 weak.^{4}

_____ 14. She^1 had^2 never^3 been^4 there^5 before.^{6}

_____ 15. Come^1 along.^{2}

_____ 16. The^1 paper^2 may^3 have^4 been^5 copied^6 from^7 somewhere^8 else.^{9}

_____ 17. Probably,^{1} the^2 teacher^3 was^4 being^5 clever.^{6}

_____ 18. Across^1 the^2 street^3 there^4 was^5 much^6 confusion.^{7}

_____ 19. The^1 ransom^2 should^3 never^4 have^5 been^6 paid.^{7}

_____ 20. The^1 men^2 had^3 seldom^4 been^5 given^6 better^7 treatment.^{8}

Exercises for
5. SUBJECTS AND VERBS

Directions: In the space at the far left write the number that represents the subject. In the remaining blanks write the index numbers that represent the complete verb.

Subject   Complete verb

____   __ __ __ __   1. Letters[1] have[2] been[3] sent[4] to[5] all[6] staff[7] members.[8]

____   __ __ __ __   2. Down[1] from[2] the[3] north[4] swept[5] the[6] mighty[7] gale.[8]

____   __ __ __ __   3. There[1] have[2] never[3] been[4] so[5] few[6] candidates.[7]

____   __ __ __ __   4. He[1] should[2] never[3] have[4] admitted[5] his[6] error.[7]

____   __ __ __ __   5. Few[1] of[2] us[3] are[4] perfect.[5]

____   __ __ __ __   6. Mid-term[1] cards[2] will[3] be[4] sent[5] to[6] departments.[7]

____   __ __ __ __   7. Never[1] have[2] I[3] seen[4] such[5] enthusiasm.[6]

____   __ __ __ __   8. There[1] you[2] have[3] the[4] solution.[5]

____   __ __ __ __   9. Each[1] of[2] the[3] members[4] should[5] assume[6] responsibility.[7]

____   __ __ __ __   10. The[1] game[2] should[3] certainly[4] never[5] have[6] been[7] lost.[8]

____   __ __ __ __   11. I[1] may[2] be[3] able[4] to[5] go[6] tomorrow.[7]

____   __ __ __ __   12. What[1] shall[2] I[3] do?[4]

____   __ __ __ __   13. Here[1] might[2] be[3] seen[4] the[5] sudden[6] shifting[7] of[8] fortune.[9]

____   __ __ __ __   14. There[1] is[2] a[3] tavern[4] in[5] the[6] town.[7]

____   __ __ __ __   15. No[1] man[2] has[3] ever[4] yet[5] become[6] great[7] by[8] imitation.[9]

____   __ __ __ __   16. This[1] is[2] an[3] easy[4] sentence.[5]

121

Exercises for

6. SUBJECTS AND VERBS

Directions: In the space at the far left write the index number that represents the subject. In the remaining blanks write the index numbers that represent the complete verb.

Subject   Complete verb

——   —————   1. The[1] old[2] gentleman[3] had[4] not[5] wanted[6] me[7] to[8] go.[9]

——   —————   2. It[1] might[2] have[3] been[4] lost[5] in[6] the[7] mail.[8]

——   —————   3. Seldom[1] have[2] I[3] seen[4] such[5] hailstones.[6]

——   —————   4. There[1] may[2] have[3] been[4] only[5] five[6] men[7] in[8] the[9] line.[10]

——   —————   5. Without[1] encouragement[2] your[3] book[4] could[5] never[6] have[7] been[8] written[9].

——   —————   6. A[1] quarter[2] of[3] an[4] hour[5] is[6] enough.[7]

——   —————   7. Some[1] of[2] the[3] students[4] had[5] been[6] lost[7] on[8] the[9] mountain.[10]

——   —————   8. Neither[1] of[2] the[3] articles[4] should[5] have[6] been[7] sold[8] for[9] that[10] price.[11]

——   —————   9. All[1] of[2] the[3] members[4] were[5] sent[6] notices.[7]

——   —————   10. Across[1] the[2] river[3] lay[4] an[5] old[6] barge.[7]

——   —————   11. Our[1] family[2] had[3] been[4] trying[5] to[6] move[7] for[8] several[9] years.[10]

——   —————   12. Will[1] you[2] be[3] sorry?[4]

——   —————   13. Few[1] of[2] us[3] have[4] been[5] selected.[6]

——   —————   14. The[1] package[2] should[3] have[4] been[5] delivered[6] yesterday.[7]

Exercises for

7. SUBJECTS AND VERBS

Directions: In the space at the far left write the index number that represents the subject. In the remaining blanks write the index numbers that represent the complete verb.

Subject   Complete verb

____   _ _ _ _ _   1. In[1] these[2] blocks[3] sixty-six[4] cars[5] are[6] being[7] illegally[8] parked.[9]

____   _ _ _ _ _   2. The[1] old[2] elephant[3] seemed[4] tired.[5]

____   _ _ _ _ _   3. Few[1] of[2] them[3] have[4] been[5] able[6] to[7] understand[8] the[9] problem.[10]

____   _ _ _ _ _   4. Exercising[1] daily[2] makes[3] him[4] strong.[5]

____   _ _ _ _ _   5. Below[1] the[2] decks[3] the[4] temperature[5] was[6] very[7] high.[8]

____   _ _ _ _ _   6. Have[1] you[2] never[3] been[4] paid[5] for[6] your[7] last[8] job?[9]

____   _ _ _ _ _   7. His[1] guilty[2] secret[3] was[4] soon[5] discovered.[6]

____   _ _ _ _ _   8. I[1] tried[2] to[3] understand[4] his[5] problem.[6]

____   _ _ _ _ _   9. That[1] criminal[2] must[3] have[4] been[5] punished[6] enough[7] by[8] now.[9]

____   _ _ _ _ _   10. Gone[1] are[2] the[3] days[4] of[5] the[6] jack-of-all-trades.[7]

____   _ _ _ _ _   11. We[1] hope[2] to[3] wake[4] him[5] up[6] soon.[7]

____   _ _ _ _ _   12. Several[1] times[2] he[3] has[4] acted[5] as[6] a[7] Turkish[8] interpreter.[9]

____   _ _ _ _ _   13. Many[1] of[2] them[3] have[4] been[5] very[6] active[7] in[8] politics.[9]

____   _ _ _ _ _   14. Have[1] you[2] been[3] talking[4] to[5] Andrew?[6]

____   _ _ _ _ _   15. By[1] the[2] end[3] of[4] the[5] year[6] many[7] houses[8] will[9] have[10] been[11] built[12] in[13] that[14] area.[15]

____   _ _ _ _ _   16. Slowly[1] the[2] stevedore[3] laid[4] his[5] heavy[6] burden[7] down.[8]

____   _ _ _ _ _   17. Under[1] the[2] stairs[3] is[4] a[5] small[6] closet.[7]

____   _ _ _ _ _   18. Many[1] have[2] been[3] called.[4]

123

Exercises for

8. SUBJECTS AND VERBS

Directions: In the space at the far left write the index number that represents the subject. In the remaining blanks write the index numbers that represent the complete verb.

Subject   Complete verb

—— ———— 1. For[1] several[2] months[3] Margaret[4] had[5] fought[6] the[7] idea.[8]

—— ———— 2. The[1] old[2] mine[3] must[4] have[5] been[6] worked[7] by[8] the[9] Spaniards.[10]

—— ———— 3. The[1] last[2] paper[3] had[4] now[5] been[6] written.[7]

—— ———— 4. Through[1] the[2] halls[3] there[4] rang[5] a[6] shot.[7]

—— ———— 5. Much[1] is[2] left[3] out[4] of[5] his[6] report.[7]

—— ———— 6. This[1] problem[2] has[3] not[4] been[5] carefully[6] considered.[7]

—— ———— 7. Father[1] may[2] have[3] been[4] too[5] harsh.[6]

—— ———— 8. Down[1] the[2] steps[3] tripped[4] the[5] lovely[6] princess.[7]

—— ———— 9. Is[1] that[2] cake[3] yours?[4]

—— ———— 10. Not[1] one[2] of[3] them[4] had[5] ever[6] been[7] consulted[8] about[9] the[10] change.[11]

—— ———— 11. Certainly[1] you[2] have[3] a[4] right[5] to[6] your[7] opinion.[8]

—— ———— 12. Some[1] of[2] us[3] could[4] not[5] agree[6] with[7] him.[8]

—— ———— 13. Many[1] were[2] not[3] sure[4] about[5] his[6] position.[7]

—— ———— 14. You[1] have[2] certainly[3] been[4] very[5] cooperative.[6]

—— ———— 15. Shall[1] you[2] be[3] able[4] to[5] go?[6]

—— ———— 16. Only[1] occasionally[2] have[3] we[4] experienced[5] such[6] excitement.[7]

—— ———— 17. Both[1] could[2] have[3] been[4] sent[5] to[6] the[7] galleys[8] for[9] life.[10]

—— ———— 18. His[1] leaving[2] early[3] has[4] always[5] been[6] a[7] source[8] of[9] annoyance[10] to[11] me.[12]

ADJECTIVES AND ADVERBS

Upon the base of the subject and verb, complicated sentence patterns may be constructed. One of the methods of expansion is by the use of adjectives and adverbs. The adjective modifies a noun or pronoun. The adverb modifies a verb, adjective, or another adverb.

In order to determine whether or not a word is an adjective it is helpful to ask if it means *what kind of* ( ). In the parenthesis supply the noun or pronoun, remembering that a noun is the name of a person, place, or thing, and the pronoun simply stands for a noun. If the problem is to select the adjective in such a sentence as "He was a slim young Englishman of medium height with quizzical eyes and an aquiline nose," one asks, "What kind of Englishman?" and gets the answers *young* and *slim*, both adjectives; "What kind of *height?*" *Medium*, an adjective; "What kind of eyes?" *Quizzical*, an adjective; "What kind of nose?" *Aquiline*, an adjective.

It might be assumed from a casual inspection that all adjectives precede the nouns they modify. This is not the case. Some adjectives are effectively used in an appositive position. "In the cellar, *dank* and *still*, there was the sound of intermittent rifle fire." "While he hid, *cold, wet,* and *forlorn*, the enemy crept through the marsh." These are sentence patterns that students could use more frequently.

Adjectives are frequently found in the predicate position; that is, they follow a linking verb and describe the subject. Study the following sentences. "The foyer was *dark*." "It was *grotesque* indeed." "His muscles showed *gaunt*." "He appeared definitely *weaker*." It is easy to see that these italicized words are adjectives modifying the subject if one asks "What kind of foyer?" The answer, a *dark* foyer, shows this to be an adjective. The name *predicate adjective* is commonly given to adjectives used in this manner. Practice using adjectives after the following verbs: *become, seem, remain, feel, sound, turn, taste, look, smell, wax,* and *stand*. Be sure that the word following the verb describes the subject and does not name something.

Passive verbs are also sometimes followed by predicate adjectives. A passive verb is used when the subject is the thing acted upon. To see the difference, compare the active verb in the sentence "The boy *hit* the ball" with the passive verb in the sentence "The ball *was hit* by the boy." Passive verbs always contain some form of the verb *to be.* The following sentences show how a predicate adjective may follow a passive verb. "The house was painted *green.*" "The boy has been called *dumb.*" "The egg should never have been boiled *hard.*"

A, an, and *the,* and the possessive pronouns are to be considered as adjectives.

The second type of word used to expand the basic framework of the sentence is the adverb. A common test to help ascertain whether or not a word is an adverb is to ask if it tells *how, when* or *where.* Thus in the sentence "He runs fast" ask "Runs how?" The answer, *fast,* shows *fast* to be an adverb modifying the verb *runs.* In the sentence "He runs now" ask "Runs when?" The answer shows that *now* is an adverb. In the sentence "He runs away" *where* may be used to test whether or not the word *away* is an adverb. By using the same three words, *how, when,* or *where,* one may determine if a word is an adverb modifying an adjective or an adverb. Take the sentence "I think she is too thin." You will, of course, recognize that *thin* is a predicate adjective. Because *too* tells how thin she is, you see at once that *too* is an adverb modifying an adjective. Or take such a sentence as "They moved too far away." Think it through in this way. They moved where? Away. Hence *away* is an adverb modifying the verb *moved.* Away where? Far. Hence *far* is an adverb modifying the adverb *away.* How far? Too far. Hence *too* is an adverb modifying another adverb.

You will observe that a great many adverbs end in *ly,* but do not jump to the conclusion that all words that end in *ly* are adverbs. For example, the word *lovely* in the sentence "I saw a lovely landscape" is not an adverb but an adjective. Notice that it tells what kind of landscape.

Yes, no, and *not* are usually adverbs, but this is as good a time as any other to point out that words in English have a disconcerting habit of being one part of speech most of the time but occasionally becoming something else entirely. One might, for instance, speak of a "yes" man, using *yes* as an adjective. A further danger that can arise if one assumes that a part of speech is always the same regardless of the way it is used in the sentence is seen in the use of nouns as adverbs. Certain nouns expressing *extent, time,* or *place* are adverbs. They are commonly called adverbial nouns. Examples are "They walked three *miles.*" "He smokes twenty cigarettes a *day.*" "The cat ran *home.*"

Exercises for

1. ADJECTIVES AND ADVERBS

Directions: In the blank space before each sentence, write 1 if the italicized word is used as an adjective, 2 if the word is used as an adverb.

_____ 1. Mrs. Davis came _out_ holding a dish cloth in her hand.

_____ 2. "Are you _comfortable?_" he asked.

_____ 3. Sit _back_ and relax.

_____ 4. Jim drank in the _lovely_ smell of roasting beef.

_____ 5. The captain stepped _inside_.

_____ 6. You must be very _quiet_.

_____ 7. By a miracle the car was _there_ when we needed it.

_____ 8. Miss Poindexter smoothed her _clean_, white gloves.

_____ 9. Now, I am _surely_ trapped.

_____ 10. By Saturday she felt very _restless_.

_____ 11. The lemonade tasted a little _sour_ to me.

_____ 12. Both students were thinking _hard_.

_____ 13. The mountain looked _solid_.

_____ 14. We had _only_ four minutes to reach the station.

_____ 15. The surf sounded _loud_ in his ears.

_____ 16. He told us that the geese were _really_ worth only four dollars.

_____ 17. At least, Jane thought _miserably_, it will be warm.

_____ 18. Indeed, it seemed very _warm_.

_____ 19. Under his influence she felt _very_ calm.

_____ 20. Iris followed the guide _up_ and down.

_____ 21. _Any_ money you find belongs to me.

_____ 22. We brought cakes and cookies for _his_ children.

Exercises for

2. ADJECTIVES AND ADVERBS

Directions: In the blank space before each sentence write 1 if the italicized word is used as an adjective, 2 if the word is used as an adverb.

_____ 1. Lizzie smiled *broadly* to herself.

_____ 2. The two ladies confronted each other in the *warm* kitchen.

_____ 3. The cat sleeps *here* at night.

_____ 4. Junior had a *sly* look on his face.

_____ 5. Doesn't she look *fierce?*

_____ 6. He is *always* blamed for everything.

_____ 7. We *never* call her Sal.

_____ 8. The stew seethed *slowly* over the fire.

_____ 9. The *lively* frog jumped over the edge of the box.

_____ 10. Ralph's face grew *rigid* from the strain.

_____ 11. The house was always very *hot*.

_____ 12. *Immediately,* Mother began to rock back and forth.

_____ 13. I can see that Joe is getting *better*.

_____ 14. We hope that you will visit us *again*.

_____ 15. The whole room was *fragrant* with the scent of sweet peas.

_____ 16. She sat *back* and gazed at the clock.

_____ 17. He was *quick* to spot an error.

_____ 18. Henry, step *inside* and sign the papers.

_____ 19. The chairs stood about in their accustomed, *exact*, right places.

_____ 20. I have always got along *very* well with our cook.

_____ 21. In the dark *all* cats are grey.

_____ 22. Please hand this in *today*.

Exercises for

3. ADJECTIVES AND ADVERBS

Directions: In the blank space before each sentence write 1 if the italicized word is used as an adjective, 2 if the word is used as an adverb.

_____ 1. The sky was _blue_.

_____ 2. It was _definitely_ a warm-hearted response.

_____ 3. The quarterback has _ice_ water in his veins.

_____ 4. Walter waxed _eloquent_ on his favorite subject.

_____ 5. The _only_ face missing was that of Stevens.

_____ 6. Edison explained his _tireless_ reading of scientific journals.

_____ 7. He sought to avoid _useless_ repetition of old experiments.

_____ 8. The _broker's_ fee amounted to six hundred dollars.

_____ 9. The lawn furniture was painted _green_.

_____ 10. Rusty came by his nickname _honestly_.

_____ 11. Admiring glances _often_ follow this car.

_____ 12. Expenses of the play were extremely _high_.

_____ 13. Natives extended the explorer a _friendly_ welcome.

_____ 14. Don't accuse me of leaving you _out_.

_____ 15. You probably know this music pretty _well_.

_____ 16. Jimmie was obviously an _only_ child.

_____ 17. His commissions at the end of the month were _very_ little.

_____ 18. A woman would recall _precisely_ what her hostess was wearing.

_____ 19. _Presently_, Mrs. Smith said that she would write another letter.

_____ 20. You should plow this soil _deep_.

_____ 21. The water tasted _warm_ and slightly muddy.

_____ 22. The accused man stood _silent_.

Exercises for

4. ADJECTIVES AND ADVERBS

Directions: In the blank space before each sentence, write 1 if the italicized word is used as an adjective, 2 if the word is used as an adverb.

_____ 1. He then asked about possible manuscripts in _private_ hands.

_____ 2. "_Now_," said Mrs. Ford, "do you have any serious objections?"

_____ 3. Mr. James brought his _early_ vegetables to market.

_____ 4. _Several_ women fainted in the crush.

_____ 5. Now, he _never_ smiles.

_____ 6. That woman is the _richest_ one of the group.

_____ 7. I am seldom _too_ busy to help.

_____ 8. Firecrackers were popping _here_ and there.

_____ 9. We brought a bone for _their_ dog.

_____ 10. Soon the elevator began to go _down_.

_____ 11. _Most_ men would do the same, I think.

_____ 12. _How_ could you do this to me?

_____ 13. All the flowers looked _fresh_ and beautiful.

_____ 14. Such remarks would have been considered _dangerous_.

_____ 15. The night was _far_ too dark for us to see the barn.

_____ 16. I found her listening to a program called "_John's_ Other Wife."

_____ 17. _Sometimes_ we lost patience with him.

_____ 18. His children always wake up _early_.

_____ 19. The _early_ bird gets the worm.

_____ 20. Let me know _soon_, won't you?

_____ 21. Harrison was _almost_ always right.

_____ 22. She wore a plain _summer_ frock.

Exercises for

5. ADJECTIVES AND ADVERBS

Directions: In the blank space before each sentence, write 1 if the italicized word is used as an adjective, 2 if the word is used as an adverb.

_____ 1. His once brick-red hair now appears *grey*.

_____ 2. "Go *ahead*," the conductor shouted.

_____ 3. Harvey won *his* first fight.

_____ 4. The company lashed *back* at its critics.

_____ 5. The right halfback played *well*.

_____ 6. After a *little* sleep we awoke refreshed.

_____ 7. Labor unity is *now* closer than ever.

_____ 8. The elevator slowly started *down*.

_____ 9. This historic message was sent *off* quietly last week.

_____ 10. Some were *still* riding the ghost of the depression.

_____ 11. At that hour *early* returns will begin to come in.

_____ 12. Getting out of mud becomes far *easier*.

_____ 13. Since its publication the document has proved *valuable*.

_____ 14. They came for dinner, but they are *still* here.

_____ 15. My den is *silent* and quiet.

_____ 16. *Almost* all of us were there.

_____ 17. We wrapped the package in our *most* careful manner.

_____ 18. The present administration has been *more* successful in this matter.

_____ 19. The West's statesmen moved *fast*.

_____ 20. Roger opened the door and peered *in*.

_____ 21. They appeared only *nervous,* not alarmed.

_____ 22. This fact was *implicit* in his statement.

Exercises for

6. ADJECTIVES AND ADVERBS

Directions: In the blank space before each sentence, write 1 if the italicized word is used as an adjective, 2 if the word is used as an adverb.

_____ 1. The Indians are *sure* that the volcano is still hungry and jealous.

_____ 2. Please, Connie, don't run so *fast*.

_____ 3. We are nearly *there*.

_____ 4. The men drew their *woolen* ponchos tight against the night air.

_____ 5. Her husband *soon* came home from the hospital.

_____ 6. The old inn is *still* in the center of town.

_____ 7. Opponents thought he might very well win *again*.

_____ 8. Balcomb became a *sadder* and wiser man.

_____ 9. Our love-sick hero gazed *deep* into her eyes.

_____ 10. My grape juice still tastes *bitter*.

_____ 11. French is *seldom* heard there.

_____ 12. Throw your hat *high* in the air.

_____ 13. Phil had a *high,* squeaky voice.

_____ 14. He was thought *shrewd* enough to avoid this pitfall.

_____ 15. Locke's vocabulary is *almost* wholly abstract.

_____ 16. Put your little foot right *there*.

_____ 17. I think she is talking *yet*.

_____ 18. My visit has been very *pleasant*.

_____ 19. The trumpet sounded *loud*.

_____ 20. *Their* roots are firmly fixed in the soil.

_____ 21. *Now* is the best time to can corn.

_____ 22. That depends on *your* point of view.

PREPOSITIONAL PHRASES

A further way in which the sentence may be expanded is by the use of phrases. The two types of phrases are prepositional phrases and verbal phrases. A phrase may be defined as a group of words used as a single word.

The first type of phrase to be discussed is the prepositional phrase. It is made up of a preposition, its object, and modifiers. All prepositions have objects, and if the object is a pronoun it will be in the objective case—that is, it will be *me, you, him, her, it, them,* or *whom.* In order to determine if a word is a preposition, look to see if it has an object. To do this it is necessary to ask "*What?*" after the preposition. If there is an answer, that answer is the object of the preposition. For example, the following are prepositional phrases: *on the table, through the window, by the stream, over the fence, according to him, during the disastrous flood.* If you ask "*On what?*" the answer, *table,* gives you the object of the preposition. Words commonly used as prepositions are listed below, but remember that these are not prepositions unless they have objects. "I looked across," for example, may be compared with "I looked across the street." The first *across* is an adverb; the second is a preposition with an object, *street.*

1. <u>Prepositional phrases may be used as nouns.</u>

Examples: In the cellar was the place   Subject
     he feared to be.
    After your nap will be soon   Subject
     enough.
    I said *after dinner,* not *after*   Direct object
     lunch.   See next section
    The best time is *in the early*   Predicate nominative
     morning.   See next section
    His office hours, *from eight*   Apposition
     to five, were filled.

2. <u>Prepositional phrases may be used as adjectives.</u>

Examples:	The man *with the gas mask* is an air warden.	Modifies *man.*
	They opened the door *at the end of the hall.*	Modify *door* and *end.*
	The book *on the desk* lay unopened.	Modifies *book.*
	The statement was *without support.*	Predicate adjective.
	The paper was *of little interest.*	Predicate adjective.
	His murder became *of no importance.*	Predicate adjective.

3. <u>Prepositional phrases may be used as adverbs.</u>

Examples:	*In our Parliament* we speak freely.	Modifies the verb, *speak.*
	They walked *into danger with open eyes.*	Both modify *walked.*
	An angel flew *over Bald Mountain.*	Modifies *flew.*
	Bill gave the ball *to me.*	Modifies *gave.*
	There was a flea *on her hat.*	Modifies *was.*
	Be honest *in your service.*	Modifies the predicate adjective *honest.*
	He was careful *with the objective case.*	Modifies *careful.*

In addition to the adjective and adverb modifiers that may be included in the prepositional phrase, the whole prepositional phrase may be modified by such adverbs as *exactly, only, just, truly, certainly, partly,* etc. Also, the preposition itself may be modified by an adverb as in the following sentences. "He stood *almost* under the bridge." "They lived *far* from the wicked city."

Usually the preposition comes before its object, but this is not always true. The sentence "What did you pay for?" is equivalent to "You did pay for what." *What* then, is seen to be the object of the preposition.

Words Commonly Used as Prepositions

about	contrary to	regarding
above	despite	regardless of
according to	down	relative to
across	during	respecting
after	for	round
against	from	since
along	in	through
amid	including	throughout
among	inside	till
around	inside of	to
aside	instead of	toward
at	into	towards
before	like	under
behind	near	underneath
below	next to	until
beneath	notwithstanding	unto
beside	of	up
besides	off	up against
between	on	upon
beyond	onto	with
by	over	within
concerning	past	without

Exercises for

1. PREPOSITIONAL PHRASES

Directions: In the blank space at the far left write the index number of the preposition in each sentence. In the second blank write the index number of the object of the preposition.

__ __ 1. Anderson[1] worked[2] in[3] a[4] London[5] advertising[6] agency.[7]

__ __ 2. Mother[1] slowly[2] came[3] down[4] the[5] rickety[6] porch[7] steps.[8]

__ __ 3. I[1] saw[2] her[3] last[4] sometime[5] in[6] June.[7]

__ __ 4. Quickly,[1] sister[2] turned[3] toward[4] Jeanie,[5] her[6] neighbor.[7]

__ __ 5. Before[1] sundown,[2] all[3] the[4] men[5] had[6] returned[7] home.[8]

__ __ 6. The[1] boys[2] scurried[3] across[4] the[5] street.[6]

__ __ 7. One[1] of[2] the[3] many[4] things[5] I[6] like[7] is[8] his[9] determination.[10]

__ __ 8. We[1] both[2] have[3] confidence[4] in[5] him.[6]

__ __ 9. Considering[1] the[2] late[3] hour,[4] you[5] had[6] better[7] go.[8]

__ __ 10. My[1] wife[2] was[3] listening[4] to[5] the[6] radio[7] when[8] the[9] announcement[10] was[11] made.[12]

__ __ 11. We[1] began[2] chewing[3] the[4] rag[5] about[6] Piltdown[7] man.[8]

__ __ 12. Like[1] her[2] brother[3] she[4] had[5] dark[6] hair[7] and[8] brown[9] eyes.[10]

__ __ 13. The[1] *Sea Venture*[2] was[3] sent[4] out[5] by[6] the[7] Virginia[8] Company.[9]

__ __ 14. Many[1] private[2] fortunes[3] were[4] founded[5] on[6] privateering.[7]

__ __ 15. Underneath[1] his[2] rough[3] exterior[4] beats[5] a[6] gentlemanly[7] heart,[8] I[9] am[10] sure.[11]

Exercises for
2. PREPOSITIONAL PHRASES

Directions: In the blank space at the far left write the index number of the preposition in each sentence. In the second blank write the index number of the object of the preposition.

— — 1. My[1] Uncle[2] David[3] is[4] just[5] like[6] your[7] father.[8]

— — 2. Slowly[1] the[2] Nautilus[3] sank[4] below[5] the[6] surface.[7]

— — 3. The[1] children[2] started[3] jumping[4] up[5] and[6] down[7] until[8] father[9] gave[10] them[11] the[12] candy[13] he[14] had[15] brought[16] with[17] him.[18]

— — 4. The[1] team[2] pulled[3] in[4] amid[5] much[6] shouting.[7]

— — 5. I[1] always[2] wanted[3] someone[4] to[5] play[6] with[7] me.[8]

— — 6. The[1] gadget[2] cost[3] four[4] dollars[5] and[6] forty[7] cents[8] including[9] the[10] tax.[11]

— — 7. Four hundred thousand[1] people[2] passed[3] through[4] the[5] turnstiles[6] that[7] year.[8]

— — 8. Natives[1] had[2] never[3] seen[4] such[5] a[6] rain[7] during[8] September.[9]

— — 9. Thick,[1] curly[2] hair[3] grew[4] around[5] his[6] ears.[7]

— — 10. In[1] the[2] early[3] morning[4] is[5] the[6] best[7] time[8] to[9] study[10] birds.[11]

— — 11. Grandpa[1] used[2] to[3] take[4] us[5] to[6] the[7] circus.[8]

— — 12. Imagine[1] that[2] house[3] without[4] mother![5]

— — 13. Quickly,[1] the[2] thief[3] glanced[4] down[5] the[6] long dark[8] hall.[9]

— — 14. Since[1] our[2] coming[3] he[4] has[5] not[6] had[7] much[8] time.[9]

— — 15. The[1] commander[2] kept[3] strictly[4] to[5] himself.[6]

Exercises for
3. PREPOSITIONAL PHRASES

Directions: In the blank space at the far left write the index number of the preposition in each sentence. In the second blank write the index number of the object of the preposition.

__ __ 1. Let[1] us[2] keep[3] this[4] a[5] secret[6] between[7] us.[8]

__ __ 2. Nearly[1] everyone[2] had[3] gone[4] except[5] Janet.[6]

__ __ 3. Suppose[1] we[2] go[3] across[4] the[5] street.[6]

__ __ 4. Father[1] backed[2] the[3] team[4] against[5] the[6] old[7] hitching[8] post.[9]

__ __ 5. I[1] left[2] her[3] without[4] a[5] word.[6]

__ __ 6. "Hop[1] in,"[2] said[3] Mr. Jenkins,[4] "and[5] I'll[6] take[7] you[8] to[9] my[10] house."[11]

__ __ 7. But[1] I[2] wouldn't[3] dream[4] of[5] going[6] there.[7]

__ __ 8. He[1] is[2] still[3] highly[4] regarded[5] notwithstanding[6] his[7] recent[8] conviction.[9]

__ __ 9. Mother[1] wanted[2] to[3] move[4] to[5] Denver.[6]

__ __ 10. You[1] will[2] see[3] a[4] large[5] number[6] of[7] these[8] new[9] foreign[10] cars.[11]

__ __ 11. Uncle[1] Henry[2] sat[3] down[4] slowly[5] and[6] placed[7] his[8] feet[9] on[10] my[11] mother's[12] best[13] sofa.[14]

__ __ 12. After[1] all,[2] you[3] should[4] be[5] more[6] agreeable.[7]

__ __ 13. I[1] heard[2] about[3] your[4] very[5] unusual[6] problem.[7]

__ __ 14. The[1] dean[2] treated[3] me[4] like[5] an[6] old[7] friend.[8]

__ __ 15. These[1] shirts[2] are[3] made[4] of[5] fine[6] imported[7] and[8] domestic[9] materials.[10]

Exercises for

4. PREPOSITIONAL PHRASES

Directions: In the blank space at the far left write the index number of the preposition in each sentence. In the second blank write the index number of the object of the preposition.

—— 1. The[1] chicken[2] rode[3] off[4] perched[5] on[6] the[7] rear[8] bumper.[9]

—— 2. This[1] new[2] house[3] is[4] certainly[5] keyed[6] to[7] contemporary[8] living.[9]

—— 3. I[1] was[2] ready[3] for[4] him.[5]

—— 4. Walt[1] pulled[2] the[3] struggling[4] fish[5] from[6] the[7] water.[8]

—— 5. The[1] tall[2] preacher[3] asked[4] heavenly[5] mercy[6] for[7] everyone[8] there.[9]

—— 6. All[1] through[2] everything[3] the[4] baby[5] slept[6] quietly.[7]

—— 7. My[1] sister[2] sweeps[3] the[4] dirt[5] underneath[6] the[7] living-room[8] rug.[9]

—— 8. About[1] our[2] little[3] room[4] were[5] scattered[6] the[7] possessions[8] that[9] my[10] roommate,[11] Joseph Bottleman,[12] had[13] left.[14]

—— 9. He[1] replied,[2] off[3] the[4] record,[5] that[6] he[7] had[8] voted[9] to[10] have[11] the[12] restrictions[13] removed.[14]

—— 10. The[1] judge[2] asked[3] him[4] what[5] he[6] had[7] done[8] before[9] that.[10]

—— 11. The[1] time[2] is[3] past[4] three[5] o'clock.[6]

—— 12. Prove[1] to[2] yourself[3] what[4] we[5] say.[6]

—— 13. It[1] is[2] fun[3] to[4] survey[5] life[6] from[7] a[8] front[9] porch.[10]

—— 14. Big[1] John[2] just[3] scratched[4] his[5] head[6] under[7] his[8] wide-brimmed[9] hat.[10]

—— 15. We[1] have[2] little[3] time[4] for[5] entertaining.[6]

COMPLEMENTS

Another means of expanding the sentence is by means of complements. The verbs in some sentences do not need additional words to make the meaning complete. The subject and verb alone express a complete thought. "The apple shone," "The window broke," "The elephant never forgot" are samples of sentences containing verbs that express a complete predication. A great many verbs, however, require the addition of substantives or adjectives to complete the meaning. A substantive is any word or group of words equivalent to a noun. Thus a noun, a pronoun, or a noun phrase is a substantive. Other types of constructions which are substantives will be discussed under verbals and clauses.

If one starts with subjects and verbs like the following, he must supply an additional word or additional words to make a complete sentence.

James threw ———————————————————.
The student wrote ———————————————.
Sullivan smacked ——————————————.

Probably any words supplied here will tell what receives the action of the verb. In other terms, you will have someone doing something to something. The someone who performs the act is the subject; the act is the verb; and the thing that receives the action is the direct object. Notice that there are always two different substantives mentioned; the direct object does not name the same thing as the subject. It is true that an apparent exception occurs in such a sentence as "He hit himself," but basically this is the same as "He hit the ball." Someone is doing something to something.

The common test to determine whether or not the verb has a direct object is to repeat the verb and ask "What?" The answer, because it tells what receives the action of the verb, will give you the direct object. In the sentences given above, read "What?" in each blank. "James threw what?" "The student wrote what?" "Sullivan smacked what?" You will perhaps get complete sentences similar to "James threw the *ball*," "The student wrote a *letter*," "Sullivan smacked a *double*." These italicized words are direct objects. They are always substantives. For example, in addition to nouns, pronouns may be used as direct objects. "I hit *him*" is a sample. In place of *him* one could supply any pronoun in the objective case, *me, him, her,*

141

it, us, them, or *whom.* If *whom* were used as the direct object, the sentence would have to read something like "*Whom* did I hit?" Rearranged, this would read "I did hit *whom.*" Remember that any word or group of words that names the receiver of the action is a direct object and must be a substantive, a noun equivalent.

Predicate Nominatives

The predicate nominative (also called the subjective complement) occurs after linking verbs and certain passive verbs. If one takes subjects and verbs like the following, he must supply a word or group of words to complete the meaning.

Jane was _____.

He became _____.

He was proved _____.

Like verbs that take a direct object, these also need words to complete them, but it is not possible here to supply words that name the receiver of the action. It would be obviously impossible to think of something receiving the action of *wasing,* or *becoming,* or *was proving.* Try filling in a substantive (noun or noun equivalent) in the above blanks. You will see at once that it is not possible to have the subject doing something to something. Instead, the substantive will name over again the subject. Indeed, many of the sentences containing a predicate nominative can be turned around without changing the meaning. Consider the sentence "Her name was Molly." *Molly* is the predicate nominative. Turn it around so that it reads "Molly was her name." *Name* is the predicate nominative. In just this way every predicate nominative names over again, or is equal to, the subject.

The predicate nominative is always a substantive. If a pronoun is used as a predicate nominative, it will occur after some form of the verb *be.* In formal usage it will always be in the nominative case. That is, it will always be *I, you, he, she, it, we, they,* or *who.* Consider the following: "I am *he.*" "You are *she.*" "It was *they.*" "It may be *he.*" "*Who* could it have been?" Notice that these are all pronouns in the nominative case after various forms of the verb *be.*

Following is a list of some of the verbs that may take predicate nominatives or predicate adjectives. There is no essential difference between the predicate nominative and the predicate adjective. One is a substantive: the other is an adjective. One names the same thing as the subject; the other describes the subject.

appear	go	prove	sound
be	grow	rank	stand
become	keep	remain	stay
fall	look	seem	taste
feel	loom	smell	turn

Occasionally the predicate nominative is introduced by *as*. Examples are "He was regarded as a veritable *giant*." "She was elected as *secretary*." "They remained as a *guard*." "He went out as *mate*." Note that these sentences are not the same as "He worked as a carpenter." "He fought as a professional." These are to be expanded to read "He worked as a carpenter works." "He fought as a professional fights." This construction will be covered under the discussion of adverbial clauses.

Indirect Objects

The indirect object tells *to* or *for* whom the direct object is designated or intended. It is always in the objective case, which means that if it is a pronoun it will be *me, you, him, her, it, us, the,* or *whom*. It is always a substantive.

The following sentence illustrates the way indirect objects are used in the sentence. Start with a sentence containing a direct object as follows: "Konsky tossed a pass." Here *pass*, because it tells what Konsky tossed, is easily recognized as a direct object. Now to show to or for whom the direct object, *pass*, was intended, we insert a substantive. "Konsky tossed *Shea* a pass." The receiver of the pass is Shea. *Shea* is the indirect object.

To test an indirect object supply *to* or *for* before the expression. It will not change the meaning of the sentence, but will prove whether or not the construction is an indirect object. Notice that the *to* or *for* is not present in the original sentence. If it is, you may regard the construction simply as a prepositional phrase used as an adverb.

Study the following sentences containing indirect objects. See whether you can supply *to* or *for* as a test.

Give the *treasurer* the bill for the things we ordered.
Will you please get *me* a new magazine?
The kind-hearted old gentleman gave *Tommy* a dime.
Why don't you tell *us* a story, Daddy?
Bring *mother and me* some peanut brittle.
He brought *himself* an overcoat.

Exercises for

1. COMPLEMENTS

Directions: In the blank space before each sentence write the number that identifies each italicized complement.

1. Direct object
2. Indirect object
3. Predicate nominative
4. Predicate adjective

_____ 1. The parents took their _children_ to the show.

_____ 2. Hopalong Cassidy helped _him_ to his horse.

_____ 3. The clerk told the _lady_ the price of the needlepoint.

_____ 4. Mrs. Rinehart was the _lady_ in the dark brown suit.

_____ 5. _Who_ are you?

_____ 6. John Sloan told _Jack_ some wild tale of danger and intrigue.

_____ 7. Among other things he painted _pictures_ of the ocean.

_____ 8. _Whom_ are you accusing?

_____ 9. It was certainly not _they_.

_____ 10. The dealer sold _them_ a large bunch of bananas.

_____ 11. The request appears _impossible_.

_____ 12. _What_ do you hear from the child?

_____ 13. The old lady would often shake her _head_ sadly.

_____ 14. Give _Aunt Martha_ this old rusty bucket.

_____ 15. Such little compliments gave _her_ courage.

_____ 16. The tackle was pictured as a _giant_.

_____ 17. Lucy was _lucky_ to have such friends.

_____ 18. Who tossed my _dog_ a bone?

Exercises for

2. COMPLEMENTS

Directions: In the blank space before each sentence write the number that identifies each italicized complement.

1. Direct object
2. Indirect object
3. Predicate nominative
4. Predicate adjective

_____ 1. The ice seemed very *thin* to me.

_____ 2. Did you put *sugar* in my coffee?

_____ 3. We gave *them* a bad scare.

_____ 4. The governor became a *candidate* for the senate.

_____ 5. The guard raised the small *horn* to his lips.

_____ 6. With every step Andrew felt *better*.

_____ 7. The house was a perfect *example* of a fourteenth-century manor house.

_____ 8. The president appointed *Robert*.

_____ 9. Mrs. Smith gave the *caretaker* a peppery lecture.

_____ 10. Christopher arranged the *luggage*.

_____ 11. A stout Frenchman gave *her* a rapturous smile.

_____ 12. Someone may be *jealous* of you.

_____ 13. After dinner the landlord appeared more *cheerful*.

_____ 14. The leader of the tribe had not deserted *them*.

_____ 15. *Whom* have you selected?

_____ 16. Friends, Romans, countrymen, lend me your *ears*.

_____ 17. Mr. and Mrs. Daniels remained our *friends*.

_____ 18. That girl never seems too *busy*.

Exercises for

3. COMPLEMENTS

Directions: In the blank space before each sentence write the number that identifies each italicized complement.

1. Direct object
2. Indirect object
3. Predicate nominative
4. Predicate adjective

_____ 1. The solution to the problem seemed *impossible*.

_____ 2. The smile left the stranger's *face*.

_____ 3. The newspaper contains *materials* of great interest.

_____ 4. In its original state Spanish moss is a long, gray, stringy *plant*.

_____ 5. The reader should be *familiar* with a variety of magazines.

_____ 6. She gave *herself* a permanent wave.

_____ 7. He hit *himself* with the golf club.

_____ 8. Mother gave the *children* supper.

_____ 9. The fish tasted *flat* without the usual sauce.

_____ 10. The meal was unusually *cheerful*.

_____ 11. The salesman swung his *cases* onto the counter.

_____ 12. She seemed *gentle*, but I had my doubts.

_____ 13. Mollie wrote *James* a letter every day.

_____ 14. I refused to give the *beggar* a dime.

_____ 15. *What* have you done to him?

_____ 16. The water from the old well tasted *bitter*.

_____ 17. The hotel furnishes its *guests* excellent accommodations.

_____ 18. Their story now appears *incredible*.

Exercises for

4. COMPLEMENTS

Directions: In the blank space before each sentence write the number that identifies each italicized complement.

1. Direct object
2. Indirect object
3. Predicate nominative
4. Predicate adjective

_____ 1. The store gave its *employees* an unusual opportunity.

_____ 2. How much *profit* did they make in 1943?

_____ 3. Won't you sing *us* an old French song?

_____ 4. The officer's face became *stern* and cold.

_____ 5. The tall, blond boy must be his *son*.

_____ 6. The company sold the *coach* a set of dumbbells.

_____ 7. He taught them *football*.

_____ 8. The attendance at the prayer meeting should have been *larger*.

_____ 9. Why not tell *Andrew* the good news?

_____ 10. At first the men appeared *awkward* and inexperienced.

_____ 11. We gave them a few *pointers* on the science of gardening.

_____ 12. Bart set his *cap* more firmly on his head.

_____ 13. The barn was painted a bright *red*.

_____ 14. The dark man was appointed as temporary *secretary*.

_____ 15. To me he always appeared very *grateful*.

_____ 16. Give *me* any information available.

_____ 17. You can give *yourself* a new permanent.

_____ 18. The drum sounded *loud* to his sensitive ears.

VERBALS

There are three kinds of verbals: participles, gerunds, and infinitives. Verbals are made from verbs but are never used as verbs. Like verbs, they may be followed by all types of complements but, unlike verbs, they are used as adjectives, nouns, or adverbs. The participle is always used as an adjective; the gerund is always used as a noun; and the infinitive may be used as a noun, adjective, or adverb.

Participles

The participle has the following forms:

present	running, playing, leaping, shouting
past	run, played, leaped, shouted
present passive	being run, being played, being leaped, being shouted
perfect participle	having run, having played, having leaped, having shouted
perfect progressive	having been running, having been shouting, having been playing, having been leaping
perfect passive	having been run, having been played, having been leaped, having been shouted

Verbs that are intransitive, that is, verbs that do not take an object, cannot have perfect progressive or perfect passive forms. Obviously it would be impossible to say *having been becoming* or *having been remained*.

You will notice that the participle may be made up of one, two, or three words. The present and the perfect progressive always end in *ing*. The other forms may end in *ed, d, de, t, en,* or in certain other letters. It may be a help to you to know that the past participle is the same form that you would use with the verb *had*. Had *gone*, had *lost*, had *stolen*, had *betrayed*, had *dug*. These are not participles as they stand. They are forms of the past perfect tense of the verb. But the second half of the verb phrase is always the form of the past participle. Historically it was a past participle, but now it simply makes one of the tenses of the verb. Present participles were also used historically to make tenses. Examples: *am running, was going, might have been playing, shall be thinking*, etc. These are not to be thought of as participles, but as complete verbs. Remember, then, that to form additional tenses the auxiliary verbs *be, do, have, may, might, can, could, still, will, would, shall*, and *should* may be added to what were originally present or past participles, but *these are not to be thought of as participles*. Only when these words modify substantives are they *participles*. Thus *gone, lost, stolen*, or *betrayed* are participles only when they mean a *gone* feeling, a *lost* book, a *stolen* horse, or a *betrayed* trust.

The participle may be used in several ways. First it may precede the word it modifies as in "A *leaping* fish made a noise in the night," "A *growling* dog kept me awake." Second it may be a participial phrase beginning the sentence and modifying the subject. Examples are "*Revealing and moving*, this book is the winner of a $1000 prize," "*Crowded with action and colorful characters*, this book takes you back to the eighteenth century," "*Surging along with irresistible force*, this book carries you along," "*Telling us a forceful story*, this book is one you will want to read." In each of these sentences the participle, together with its modifiers and complements, modifies the subject of each sentence, *book*. The participle may, in addition, occupy an appositive position. Examples: "The gardener, *having strained himself lifting the lawn roller*, was forced to stay in bed," "His suggestion, *uttered here for the first time*, was well received." "The doctor, *hastily babbling something about another patient*, fled down the hall." Also the participle may follow the word it modifies. Examples: "The man *smiling* at us in this picture is a politician," "Men *running* for office must be expert at kissing babies." Still another way in which the participle may be used is as a predicate adjective after a linking verb. "They appeared very much *discouraged*," "Mother seemed rather *tired* today," "The meat tasted *burned*."

The last way in which the participle is commonly used is in the nominative absolute construction. The nominative absolute is a substantive plus a participle, the resulting phrase having a logical connection but not a grammatical connection with the rest of the sentence. Study the following sentences:

Rain having fallen all night, we were unable to ford the stream.

The weather being much colder, he wore his overcoat.

The enemy having been driven from the hills, our forces occupied them at noon.

His work finished for the day, he sat down nervous with fatigue.

The great strike of Hawaiian pineapple workers having been settled, the men returned to work.

They set out on a brilliant blue afternoon, the day's heat having subsided.

Some of the bodies still bore marks of the last struggle, the arms flung up with the fingers clawing, the chins twisted sideways, heads straining to gasp above the water.

Gerunds

The second type of verbal is the gerund. It, like a participle, is made from a verb, but, unlike the participle, it is used as a noun. The gerund, then, is another substantive, the others we have studied being nouns, pronouns, and prepositional phrases. Since the only ways in which substantives can be used are as subjects, objects, predicate nominatives, or appositives, it follows that these are the only ways gerunds can be used.

Gerunds have the same form as the present participle; indeed, some grammars do not mention gerunds, but speak only of participles used as nouns. Since it is true that participles and gerunds look alike, it is extremely important to observe how they are used in the sentence, for only by their use in the sentence can they be identified. Study the following examples of the ways gerunds are used. Note that the gerund may be modified by adjectives and adverbs and may take most of the types of complements previously studied.

1. Subject of the sentence

   Writing an application letter proved difficult.

   Giving her an apple helped his grade.

   Becoming a soldier is a long and painful business.

2. Direct object

   We tried *giving* her vitamin pills.

   Grandma enjoyed his *singing* aloud in the evening.

   My plumber tried *turning* it off with a wrench.

3. Predicate nominative

   His hobby was *building* model airplanes.

   That is *calling* a spade a spade.

His worst habit was *sleeping* through eight o'clock classes.

4. Object of a preposition
Without *consulting* our wishes, the committee acted.
He was arrested for *violating* a traffic law.
They presented arguments against *letting* dogs run loose.

5. Appositive
His work, *repairing* typewriters, occupied all his time.

Infinitives

The third and last type of verbal is the infinitive. The present infinitive always has the form of the simple verb—the same form that you would find in the present tense, first person, of the verb. It is usually preceded by *to*, which may be called the sign of the infinitive. *To run, to play, to shout, to laugh, to dream, to hope, to fear, to write,* etc., are all infinitives, and with these no student has difficulty. Unfortunately, not all infinitives carry their mark of identification so plainly. After the verbs *let, do, make, dare* (not), *feel, hear, need, bid,* and *see* and also after the prepositions *but* and *except,* it is common to have an infinitive without the *to.* Examples: "They let him *go*," "I did nothing except *play*."

The infinitive may be followed by any type of complement, may be modified by adverbs or prepositional phrases used adverbially, or, as you will learn, may have a subject. The infinitive and its modifiers and complements make up an infinitive phrase.

Infinitives may be used as:

1. Nouns

To fly kites in the spring is one of the joys of youth.	Subject
Paul began *to earn* his own living at the age of fourteen.	Direct object
It was pleasant *to walk* along the stream. (Note that the *it* merely anticipates the infinitive phrase which is the real subject of the sentence.)	Delayed subject after *it*
His chief aim was *to play* in the Rose Bowl.	Predicate nominative
The proposal, *to table* the motion, was lost.	Appositive

She did nothing but *mope* all day. (Object of preposition *but*.)

We who are about *to die* salute you. (Object of preposition *about*.)

The infinitive very often takes a subject. This subject is in the objective case.

The company made *him resign*. (Infinitive phrase used as direct object.) *Him* is the subject of the infinitive, *resign*.

They wanted *Cliff to go*. (Infinitive phrase used as direct object.)

For him to come late is inexcusable. (Infinitive phrase as the object of the preposition *for*. The prepositional phrase, *for him to come late*, is the subject of the sentence.)

It is unnecessary for *us to be alarmed*. (Infinitive phrase used as the object of the preposition *for*. The prepositional phrase, *for us to be alarmed*, is the delayed subject of the sentence after *it*.)

Now is the time for *us to be prepared*. (Infinitive phrase used as the object of *for*. The prepositional phrase, *for us to be prepared*, modifies *time*.)

2. <u>Adjectives</u>

   Is this a good place *to go* for a picnic? (The infinitive phrase, *to go for a picnic*, modifies *place*.)

   The men *to be inducted* were given their papers. (Modifies *men*.)

   Give a man a horse *to ride*. (The infinitive modifies *horse*.)

   The baby appeared *to be lost*. (The infinitive phrase, *to be lost*, is used as the predicate adjective of the sentence.)

3. <u>Adverbs</u>

   a. Modifying a verb

      We looked in the mailbox *to see* if the package had come. (Modifies *looked*.)

      To look at him, you would think he was a senator. (Modifies *would think*.)

      Carefully, he listened *to hear* the latest news. (Modifies *listened*.)

   b. Modifying an adjective

      We shall be happy *to hear* from you. (Modifies *happy*.)

      He is slow *to anger*. (Modifies *slow*.)

      It was soon ready *to serve* for lunch. (Modifies *ready*.)

   c. Modifying an adverb

      Is it too late *to go* to a show? (Modifies the adverb *too*.)

      He was kind enough *to wait* for me. (Modifies *enough*.)

      No one thought him so wicked as *to do* that. (Modifies *so*.)

The infinitive may take six forms. Intransitive verbs, however, have no passive forms.

    Mrs. Chittenden came *to inquire* about your cook. (Present infinitive.)

    The rats seemed *to be leaving* the ship. (Present progressive infinitive. Made up of *be* plus the present participle.)

    They seem *to have studied* the wrong lesson. (Perfect infinitive. Made up of *have* plus the past participle.)

    He was known *to have been visiting* his sister. (Perfect progressive infinitive. Made up of *have been* plus the present participle.)

    The colonel has ordered the prisoner *to be released*. (Present passive infinitive. Made up of *be* plus the past participle.)

    He appears *to have been held* without a warrant. (Perfect passive infinitive. Made up of *have been* plus the past participle.)

Exercises for

1. VERBALS

Directions: In the blank space before each sentence write the number that identifies each italicized verbal.

1. Participle
2. Gerund
3. Infinitive

_____ 1. The show was brightened by the supple *dancing* girls.

_____ 2. Have you considered *using* an electric typewriter?

_____ 3. Ask to *see* this new product.

_____ 4. The performer starts an elaborate card trick, confidently *enlisting* the aid of the audience.

_____ 5. His hobby was *building* models of all kinds of buggies and wagons.

_____ 6. *Dedicated* to the principles of the music he interprets, he is a magnificent pianist.

_____ 7. Everyone enjoys *looking* at this fine view.

_____ 8. I found it a *disgusting* study of the human race.

_____ 9. Let us *see* why he does so well.

_____ 10. *Having come* to share the same feeling, we were not surprised at her rewards.

_____ 11. Soames had always wanted to write and *produce* a good play.

_____ 12. Dolores found *growing* up in poverty a difficult business.

_____ 13. No *living* writer can do it better.

_____ 14. His pipe *going* full blast, he strode angrily into the room.

_____ 15. McClellan was then a *rising* young general.

_____ 16. She could not shout loud enough to *be heard*.

_____ 17. This is a well-written paper, fully but unobtrusively *documented*.

_____ 18. Several families were engaged in *selling* perfume, tweed, and leather goods.

_____ 19. Have you tried *opening* the can with your knife?

Exercises for

2. VERBALS

Directions: In the blank space before each sentence write the number that identifies each italicized verbal.

1. Participle
2. Gerund
3. Infinitive

_____ 1. *Doing* his duty turned out to be the best thing for him.

_____ 2. The villain wore a *puzzled* expression.

_____ 3. You will enjoy its *relaxed* security.

_____ 4. The referee cautioned them against *hitting* with the closed fist.

_____ 5. We saw them *come* down the aisle.

_____ 6. This policy gives you *limited* protection.

_____ 7. We left after *having written* two papers.

_____ 8. *Having written* on two questions, we felt that we had finished the required amount.

_____ 9. We heard Sergeant Kent *cry* for help.

_____ 10. I do not want to see you *biting* your pencils.

_____ 11. The books not *having been ordered,* you cannot blame the store.

_____ 12. You can not expect us to *take* them back.

_____ 13. *Accustomed* to hard work, the sailors did not complain.

_____ 14. Have you tried *throwing* salt over your shoulder?

_____ 15. This device is too simple to *be* helpful.

_____ 16. I hate *to be ignored.*

_____ 17. This is *going* too far.

_____ 18. By *refusing* help, you put yourself in a bad light.

_____ 19. Rain fell throughout the *running* of the race.

Exercises for

3. VERBALS

<u>Directions</u>: In the blank space before each sentence write the number that identifies each italicized verbal.

1. Participle
2. Gerund
3. Infinitive

_____ 1. The case is light enough to *carry* on a plane.

_____ 2. He looks *tired*.

_____ 3. *Denouncing* the impostor proved harder than I had thought.

_____ 4. She succeeded only in *adding* to her own duties.

_____ 5. *Made* from selected cherries, this pie is sure to please you.

_____ 6. Let us *shout* this good news from the roof.

_____ 7. Most of us are kept from *making* such foolish statements.

_____ 8. *Looking* more dead than alive, Homer was carried from the field.

_____ 9. The game *having been lost,* we folded our arms and sat silent.

_____ 10. She is like a pioneer woman *swinging* her axe around.

_____ 11. We began *shouting* instructions to him.

_____ 12. This is no time to *be* cautious.

_____ 13. Those *grasping* characters in Washington were blamed for all the ills.

_____ 14. His *frightened* eyes were fixed on mine.

_____ 15. "Don't worry," she said, *baring* her pearl-like teeth.

_____ 16. For *calling* them rascals she was sued for $5,000.

_____ 17. She abetted her son in his *continuing* refusal to appear before the committee.

_____ 18. Help us *list* these items, won't you?

_____ 19. *Leaving* his old friend was the hardest thing he had ever done.

Exercises for
4. VERBALS

Directions: In the blank space before each sentence write the number that identifies each italicized verbal.

1. Participle
2. Gerund
3. Infinitive

_____ 1. I'll find a way to *stop* you.

_____ 2. *Picking* up the wagon tongue, she wheeled the vehicle toward the street.

_____ 3. An intelligent force of *trained* labor is required.

_____ 4. *Flaunting* these facts is not considered good form.

_____ 5. The company was about to *establish* a small laboratory.

_____ 6. *Having been delayed,* we could not take the 5:05.

_____ 7. He rarely makes a speech without *throwing* in a quotation from Shakespeare.

_____ 8. Will you let me *see* her?

_____ 9. Her family tried *running* a grocery store.

_____ 10. Captain Harvey sailed his *converted* tuna-fish schooner to Astoria.

_____ 11. The visiting actress was beginning to *be* famous.

_____ 12. "I built my business by *batting* my eyes at purchasing agents," she said.

_____ 13. Soon she began *making* money hand over fist.

_____ 14. You will want to *wear* your new hat, Susan.

_____ 15. These small grips are used for *pulling* strands of wire through walls of skyscrapers.

_____ 16. We made her *sing* the native words.

_____ 17. The *required* reading proved extremely difficult for him.

_____ 18. I dared not *complain.*

DEPENDENT CLAUSES

The final method of expanding the simple sentence is by the use of dependent clauses. One may think of the sentence as an independent clause, that is, a clause that can stand alone. It has a subject and predicate, and it may have any of the modifiers or complements discussed in previous sections. The dependent clause is exactly like the sentence except for one very important thing—it cannot stand alone. It is dependent. It may, like the independent clause, have any of the modifiers or complements mentioned, but it does not express a complete thought. It requires the presence of the independent clause to give the entire sentence meaning. The dependent clause is kept from being a complete thought by the presence of a subordinating word expressed or understood. Some of these subordinating words follow:

Pronouns

that	whose	
who	whoever	
whom	whomever	
which	whichever	
what	whatever	

Adverbs

where
when
why
whence
whither
how

Conjunctions

as	before	after
because	than	that
though	since	lest
although	until	inasmuch as
so that	while	in order that
even if	where	provided that
even though	wherever	on condition that
as if	whither	in case that
when	whence	whenever
unless	if	till

Adjective Clauses

An adjective clause is a clause that modifies a noun or pronoun. It adds to, limits, qualifies, or changes the noun or pronoun. Like other adjective modifiers, it tells what kind of. This is the way to apply the test. In the following sentence the adjective clause is italicized. "He tried to face the new light *in which he saw the manager.*" The clause modifies *light,* a noun. One asks, "*What kind of light?*" The answer is "A light in which he saw the manager." This shows that the clause modifies a noun and proves it is an adjective clause. Study the following adjective clauses, noting that *who, whom, which, that,* and *as* are the most common subordinating words. They are pronouns and refer directly to the word the adjective clause modifies. They most logically follow the noun or pronoun they modify. Note also that the word *that* is commonly omitted.

She took Daisy to the room *which she had carefully prepared.*

He is not such a dangerous character *as people think.*

James was a driving sort of person *who had the air of being up to his ears in work.*

Bigelow was a man *whom people naturally admired.*

The train *they expected to take* was delayed by a flood.

We are equipped to take any type of picture *you prefer.*

Sometimes the pronoun used to subordinate adjective clauses is the object of a preposition. The prepositional phrase formed by the preposition and the subordinating pronoun is used adverbially to modify the verb of the dependent clause. Note that if you begin the clause with the subordinating word and end it with the preposition, the adjective clauses in the following sentences are exactly like the ones above.

The car was the same one *in which I had ridden before.*
   (This is the same as the sentence "The car was the same one which I had ridden in before.")

Biggs was a man *in whom I had a great deal of confidence.*

It was a campaign *about which one hears very little these days.*

Mr. Appleby, *from whom I purchased the seeds,* said that they would grow in this climate.

One type of adjective clause is puzzling because it begins with *when* or *where,* and students who are not careful will jump to the conclusion that such clauses are adverbial. They modify the nouns *time* or *place* or their equivalents.

I have never known a time *when conditions were more favorable.*

He knows a place *where he can get a cup of coffee for a nickel.*

It was a moment *when the whole world stood still.*

We visited the attic *where he stored his damaged furniture.*

Noun Clauses

Unlike other dependent clauses, the noun clause is an essential part of the sentence, and, except when it is used as an appositive, cannot be omitted in reading the sentence. Noun clauses are always used as substantives.

By this time you are familiar with nouns, pronouns, gerunds, certain infinitives, and certain prepositional phrases that are substantives. The list is completed with the addition of the noun clause. Like other substantives, it may be used as a subject, predicate nominative, appositive, or object. One of the ways by which you may test a noun clause is to substitute another substantive in place of the clause—for example, *it,* or such nouns as the *fact,* the *truth,* the *thing,* etc.

The sentence, "*That the subject is distasteful* is apparent," shows a noun clause as the subject of the sentence. You can supply an *it* in place of the noun clause, and the resulting sentence, "*It* is apparent," shows one substantive used in place of another and proves that the clause is a noun clause. In this same way nearly every noun clause may be tested to see that it actually is used as a substantive. A noun clause may be used as follows:

1. Subject of the sentence
   Why he failed remained a mystery.
   How she did it puzzled even me.
   Why potatoes are so scarce could not be explained.
   "*When may I see you again?*" was his last question.
   Where to place the captured tanks was the question facing the mayor.
2. Direct object of a verb or verbal
   McShane asked *who would get the contract.*
   Tell us *how we can distinguish the true from the false.*
   The fighter assumed *that the rules would be explained.*
   Believing *what seemed to her the truth,* she was naturally confused.

She wished to see *which was the better* of the two machines.

Doing *what he had been told* proved very difficult.

3. Object of a preposition

Merchants gave prizes to *whoever turned in correct answers.*

The sailor knew nothing except *what the captain had told him.*

Give the book to *whomever the instructor sends.*

Can I depend on *what you tell me?*

The souvenirs are purchased by *whoever wants a cheap reminder of the place.*

He certainly knew very little about *what I had told him.*

I could not see much from *where I stood.*

4. Predicate nominative

The remarkable thing about the music was *that it came from a cheap harmonica.*

This order is not *what it is supposed to be.*

That is *why I am here.*

These were not *what I had expected.*

The question is *"Who are they?"*

She could not help herself, being *who she was.* (Predicate nominative of the participle, *being.*)

5. Subject of infinitive

The old man made *whoever passed* pay him a tribute.

6. Predicate nominative of a verbal

I assumed this to be *what he had come for.*

7. Apposition

His request—*that he be granted leave of absence*—was referred to the committee.

8. Delayed subject after *it*

It became apparent *that he could not succeed.*

It seemed best *that we go home.*

It was obvious *how he had planned the campaign.*

It is certain *he has won a great moral victory.*

9. Indirect object of a verb or verbal

Tell *whoever comes* what I have told you.

Adverbial Clauses

The third and last type of dependent clause that you will be expected to identify is the adverbial clause. Since you can, presumably, now readily recognize adjective clauses and noun clauses, you may place all other dependent clauses into the adverbial classification—the only one left.

If this seems too easy for you, you may learn that adverbial clauses, like all other adverbial modifiers, may modify verbs, adjectives, or adverbs in other clauses.

The adverbial clause may precede the clause containing the word or words modified; it may follow the word modified; or it may be placed between the elements of another clause, as follows:

a. *If this isn't enough,* they paint pictures to express their ideas. (Modifies the verb *paint.*)

b. An exclamation of horror broke from his lips *as he saw the hideous face grinning at him.* (Modifies the verb *broke.*)

c. His paper, *if it is completed on time,* will be published in the next issue. (Modifies the verb *will be published.*)

Like adverbs, adverbial clauses may be identified by asking How? When? Where? But additional questions may also need to be asked to help you identify this type of dependent clause. Study the following adverbial clauses:

A. Modifying verbs
   1. Manner (How?)
       a. A man should write *as he talks.* (*Should write* how? *As he talks.*)
       b. *As the twig is bent,* so must it grow.
       c. The sergeant returned to his desk *as if nothing had happened.*
       d. He fought *as though he were inspired.*
   2. Time (When?)
       a. We shall go *when you are ready.* (*Shall go* when? *When you are ready.*)
       b. You had better study *while the baby sleeps.*
       c. *Before he could blink,* the disks were gone.
       d. Suddenly, *after he had raised his gun,* the animal disappeared.
   3. Place (Where?)
       a. Don looked for it *where he had left it.* (*Looked* where? *Where he had left it.*)
       b. *Wherever you go,* you will remember me.
   4. Condition (On what condition?)
       a. *If I am wrong,* you may correct me. (*May cor-*

rect on what condition? On the condition *that I am wrong.*)

    b.   Let us play nine more holes *unless you are tired.*

    c.   *Should you desire additional references,* you may write Dr. Peterson.

    5.   Purpose (For what purpose?)

        a.   The thief broke the locker *so that he might steal the tests.* (*Broke* for what purpose? *So that he might steal the tests.*)

        b.   The man in cowboy regalia held up his hand *in order that traffic might be directed.*

    6.   Result or consequence (With what result?)

        a.   He studied for long hours, *so that his parents were not surprised at his good grades.* (*Studied* with what result? With the result *that his parents were not surprised at his good grades.*)

    7.   Cause (Why?)

        a.   *Because our hearts are pure,* we fear no evil. (*Fear* why? *Because our hearts are pure.*)

        b.   I will stay *since you wish it.* (*Will stay* why? *Since you wish it.*)

        c.   *Since living quarters are scarce,* Tom and Smitty bought a trailer.

        d.   Are we mice *that we submit to such indignities?*

    8.   Concession (Admitting what?)

        a.   *Even though we may be taxed heavily,* it still appears necessary. (*admitting what?* Admitting *that we may be taxed heavily.*)

        b.   *Although we could not trust him,* we gave him the task of organizing the crew.

        c.   *Though he was no hero to his valet,* he was a great man.

        d.   *Even if Mac is proved wrong,* he would never admit his fault.

  B. Modifying adjectives

    1.   We answer such questions *as we can.* (*As we can* modifies the adjective *such.*)

    2.   Herb is confident *that he can do better.* (Modifies the predicate adjective *confident.* Adverbial clauses of this sort are commonly used to complete such predicate adjectives as *certain, confident, concerned, glad, anxious, careful, happy, sad, sorry,* etc.)

3. Bolenciecwiz was dumber *than an ox* (is dumb). (Modifies the predicate adjective *dumber* and completes the comparison.)

4. Always sleeping *when he should be studying,* John, naturally, will fail. (Modifies the participle *sleeping.*)

C. Modifying adverbs
   1. Henry is as old *as Janie.* (Modifies the adverb *as* [which modifies the predicate adjective *old*] and completes the comparison. Note that many adverbial clauses of this sort omit the verb. This omission is called ellipsis.)

   2. She is not so old *as I.* (Modifies *so;* completes the comparison.)

   3. Your theme is so dull *that I cannot read it.* (Modifies *so;* expresses result.)

   4. Writing *after you are told to stop* is forbidden. (Modifies the gerund *writing.*)

   5. She was ready to lie *if it would raise her grade.* (Modifies the infinitive *to lie.*)

Exercises for

1. DEPENDENT CLAUSES

Directions: In the blank spaces at the left write the index numbers of the words that begin and end the dependent clause in each sentence.

_____ 1. When[1] young[2] Ballou[3] left,[4] he[5] said[6] goodbye.[7]

_____ 2. The[1] man[2] who[3] repaired[4] our[5] set[6] is[7] named[8] Harms.[9]

_____ 3. That[1] you[2] are[3] absent[4] minded[5] is[6] well[7] known.[8]

_____ 4. Where[1] were[2] you[3] when[4] it[5] began[6] to[7] rain?[8]

_____ 5. In[1] the[2] dark[3] I[4] could[5] not[6] tell[7] who[8] the[9] man[10] was.[11]

_____ 6. Although[1] you[2] are[3] late,[4] I[5] must[6] forgive[7] you.[8]

_____ 7. It[1] was[2] a[3] far[4] better[5] gift[6] than[7] I[8] had[9] expected.[10]

_____ 8. Remember[1] what[2] you[3] can[4] do![5]

_____ 9. There[1] was[2] a[3] lull[4] in[5] the[6] conversation[7] while[8] the[9] lawyer[10] shuffled[11] his[12] papers.[13].

_____ 10. These[1] are[2] the[3] best[4] cookies[5] that[6] mother[7] ever[8] made.[9]

_____ 11. As[1] my[2] uncle[3] said,[4] we[5] shall[6] miss[7] our[8] Sunday[9] walks.[10]

_____ 12. Finally,[1] Clancy[2] said[3] that[4] he[5] hoped[6] to[7] prove[8] a[9] theory[10].

_____ 13. The[1] cook[2] sent[3] her[4] little[5] boy,[6] who[7] was[8] visiting[9] her,[10] to[11] see[12] about[13] the[14] queer[15] noise.[16]

_____ 14. Maple Center,[1] which[2] is[3] located[4] on[5] Highway[6] 236,[7] is[8] only[9] a[10] village.[11]

_____ 15. She[1] is[2] almost[3] as[4] tall[5] as[6] I.[7]

Exercises for

2. DEPENDENT CLAUSES

Directions: In the blank spaces at the left write the index numbers of the words that begin and end the dependent clause in each of the sentences.

___ ___ 1. That^1 was^2 how^3 the^4 accident^5 happened.^{6}

___ ___ 2. He^1 might^2 not^3 know^4 us^5 if^6 he^7 met^8 us^9 on^{10} the^{11} road.^{12}

___ ___ 3. "How^1 did^2 you^3 know?"^{4} he^5 asked.^{6}

___ ___ 4. If^1 you^2 have^3 not^4 spent^5 all^6 your^7 money,^{8} may^9 I^{10} borrow^{11} a^{12} dollar?^{13}

___ ___ 5. Wherever^1 people^2 gather,^{3} they^4 are^5 discussing^6 the^7 problem.^{8}

___ ___ 6. The^1 clerk^2 looked^3 at^4 me^5 as^6 if^7 he^8 had^9 never^{10} seen^{11} me^{12} before.^{13}

___ ___ 7. I^1 would^2 never^3 have^4 known^5 what^6 he^7 was^8 doing^9 there.^{10}

___ ___ 8. Before^1 you^2 quit,^{3} you^4 should^5 talk^6 with^7 your^8 adviser.^{9}

___ ___ 9. Let^1 us^2 visit^3 a^4 lake^5 where^6 we^7 can^8 catch^9 some^{10} fish.^{11}

___ ___ 10. This^1 is^2 about^3 the^4 best^5 broadcloth^6 that^7 ever^8 lulled^9 a^{10} man^{11} into^{12} slumber.^{13}

___ ___ 11. Send^1 the^2 box^3 C.O.D.^{4} unless^5 you^6 hear^7 from^8 me^9 before^{10} Tuesday.^{11}

___ ___ 12. Give^1 the^2 report^3 to^4 whomever^5 the^6 captain^7 sends.^{8}

___ ___ 13. I^1 can^2 tell^3 you^4 what^5 they^6 ate^7 for^8 breakfast.^{9}

___ ___ 14. As^1 she^2 sat^3 down,^{4} she^5 rustled^6 softly.^{7}

___ ___ 15. This^1 is^2 a^3 model^4 that^5 will^6 look^7 good^8 on^9 any^{10} woman.^{11}

___ ___ 16. He^1 noted^2 the^3 ever^4 increasing^5 numbers^6 of^7 men^8 of^9 property^{10} who^{11} were^{12} lovers^{13} of^{14} peace.^{15}

___ ___ 17. A^1 little^2 study^3 showed^4 that^5 a^6 great^7 revolution^8 had^9 taken^{10} place^{11} in^{12} the^{13} constitution^{14} of^{15} society.^{16}

Exercises for

3. DEPENDENT CLAUSES

Directions: In the blank spaces at the left write the index numbers of the words that begin and end the dependent clause in each of the sentences.

___ ___ 1. According¹ to² Johnny³ they⁴ walked⁵ around⁶ the⁷ countryside⁸ until⁹ they¹⁰ were¹¹ both¹² tired.¹³

___ ___ 2. I¹ must² say³ I⁴ like⁵ your⁶ little⁷ town.⁸

___ ___ 3. When¹ I² first³ saw⁴ the⁵ peaceful⁶ little⁷ town,⁸ I⁹ fell¹⁰ in¹¹ love¹² with¹³ it.¹⁴

___ ___ 4. We¹ could² not³ find⁴ a⁵ store⁶ which⁷ carried⁸ that⁹ brand.¹⁰

___ ___ 5. That¹ you² have³ delayed⁴ your⁵ departure⁶ too⁷ long⁸ is⁹ quite¹⁰ evident.¹¹

___ ___ 6. This¹ instrument² will³ give⁴ you⁵ a⁶ new⁷ concept⁸ of⁹ how¹⁰ wonderful¹¹ a¹² fine¹³ tape¹⁴ recorder¹⁵ can¹⁶ be.¹⁷

___ ___ 7. "Why¹ have² you³ come?"⁴ asked⁵ the⁶ judge.⁷

___ ___ 8. You¹ will² be³ amazed⁴ when⁵ you⁶ look⁷ through⁸ these⁹ fine¹⁰ binoculars.¹¹

___ ___ 9. A¹ man² I³ know⁴ gave⁵ it⁶ to⁷ me.⁸

___ ___ 10. It¹ is² the³ guarantee⁴ that⁵ counts.⁶

___ ___ 11. This¹ fine² tire³ wears⁴ longer⁵ than⁶ other⁷ tires.⁸

___ ___ 12. The¹ old² man³ doesn't⁴ know⁵ what⁶ has⁷ become⁸ of⁹ his¹⁰ old¹¹ friends.¹²

___ ___ 13. The¹ Ludlums² are³ buying⁴ the⁵ house⁶ though⁷ they⁸ have⁹ had¹⁰ some¹¹ difficulty¹² in¹³ securing¹⁴ a¹⁵ loan.¹⁶

___ ___ 14. It¹ was² the³ very⁴ principle⁵ upon⁶ which⁷ the⁸ law⁹ was¹⁰ established.¹¹

___ ___ 15. The¹ novel² has³ an⁴ air⁵ of⁶ authenticity⁷ even⁸ though⁹ the¹⁰ author¹¹ never¹² saw¹³ a¹⁴ battle-field.¹⁵

Exercises for

4. DEPENDENT CLAUSES

Directions: In the blank spaces at the left write the index numbers of the words that begin and end the dependent clause in each of the sentences.

—— 1. There[1] must[2] be[3] something[4] wrong[5] with[6] a[7] traveler[8] who[9] would[10] use[11] such[12] a[13] suitcase.[14]

—— 2. Ruggles[1] asked[2] how[3] I[4] proposed[5] to[6] support[7] a[8] wife.[9]

—— 3. When[1] a[2] ship[3] is[4] ready[5] to[6] be[7] unloaded,[8] an[9] inspector[10] is[11] assigned[12] to[13] every[14] eight[15] or[16] ten[17] passengers.[18]

—— 4. The[1] man[2] told[3] us[4] that[5] every[6] question[7] would[8] be[9] answered.[10]

—— 5. Deliver[1] this[2] to[3] whoever[4] calls.[5]

—— 6. This[1] recipe[2] is[3] one[4] upon[5] which[6] I[7] will[8] stake[9] my[10] reputation.[11]

—— 7. His[1] house[2] cost[3] more[4] than[5] mine.[6]

—— 8. We[1] are[2] glad[3] to[4] report[5] that[6] funds[7] have[8] been[9] voted[10] to[11] control[12] the[13] spread[14] of[15] ragweed.[16]

—— 9. The[1] lieutenant[2] commander,[3] who[4] is[5] now[6] in[7] the[8] Naval[9] Reserve,[10] was[11] called[12] to[13] active[14] duty.[15]

—— 10. The[1] place[2] sounded[3] as[4] though[5] an[6] artillery[7] barrage[8] were[9] going[10] on.[11]

—— 11. That[1] you[2] have[3] been[4] misguided[5] now[6] appears[7] certain.[8]

—— 12. At[1] the[2] park,[3] when[4] a[5] fight[6] begins,[7] someone[8] rings[9] a[10] bell.[11]

—— 13. It[1] is[2] sure[3] that[4] you[5] have[6] never[7] understood[8] this[9] before.[10]

—— 14. His[1] face,[2] as[3] he[4] swiveled[5] around[6] toward[7] Jonathan,[8] was[9] creased[10] by[11] a[12] frown.[13]

—— 15. The[1] doctor[2] shook[3] his[4] head[5] and[6] replied,[7] "I'm[8] afraid[9] not,[10] old[11] man."[12]

Exercises for
5. TYPES OF CLAUSES

Directions: In the blank write the number that identifies the type of dependent clause italicized in each sentence.

1. Adjective clause
2. Noun clause
3. Adverbial clause

_____ 1. The headwaiter bowed lower _than I have ever seen him bow._

_____ 2. Tom showed me a picture of the singer, _who was clearly a woman of over sixty._

_____ 3. The writer told me _that he had missed a jail sentence only by fast footwork._

_____ 4. Is this the light-fingered thief _who came to Denver under the name of Silk-Hat Harry?_

_____ 5. Guests were forbidden to play the piano after 11:00 P.M., _so that they would not keep other guests awake._

_____ 6. _If you had been shipwrecked on a desert island,_ could you write a three-hundred word theme about it?

_____ 7. People in Rome believed _that he was no great shakes as a fiddle player._

_____ 8. _What you will discover_ is no secret to anyone.

_____ 9. There was not another man alive _whom I could trust._

_____ 10. _Because Kratz was under suspicion of several major crimes,_ he was not the best candidate.

_____ 11. This was the first play _on which he had collaborated with Bates._

_____ 12. Tell the story to _whoever asks for it._

_____ 13. At lunch he outlined stories _until the editor begged him to stop._

_____ 14. The last book _he had read_ was Little Black Sambo.

_____ 15. _"Why did you do that?"_ asked Betty in surprise.

Exercises for

6. TYPES OF CLAUSES

Directions: In the blank write the number that identifies the type of dependent clause italicized in each sentence.

1. Adjective clause
2. Noun clause
3. Adverbial clause

_____ 1. The youth was arrested for speeding *while he was hurrying to make an eight-o'clock class.*

_____ 2. Now and then we become excited about *what they say.*

_____ 3. The coach told us *that he had given up his position after absorbing eight straight losses.*

_____ 4. At that time he met Mencken, *who was just emerging from the cub-reporter stage.*

_____ 5. Anyone *who can write home for money* can write a theme.

_____ 6. The artist was distracted *when his model insisted on bringing her dog with her.*

_____ 7. Later on, *as the student calmed down,* he realized how right his mother had been.

_____ 8. The Magistrate, *in whom we had little confidence,* gave his pompous decision.

_____ 9. Johnson said *that he was still able to blush at the memory of the score.*

_____ 10. He made some shrewd inquires about weather conditions *before he finally gave his consent.*

_____ 11. Mrs. Haines and her staff designed the costumes, *which are generally admirable.*

_____ 12. I told him *how much his praise meant to me.*

_____ 13. To his surprise he found that he could sew better *than his wife.*

_____ 14. *Although he had never before been to the ballet,* he thoroughly enjoyed the performance.

_____ 15. *What he should do about such matters* was his first problem in the new job.

Exercises for

7. TYPES OF CLAUSES

Directions: In the blank write the number that identifies the type of dependent clause italicized in each sentence.

1. Adjective clause
2. Noun clause
3. Adverbial clause

_____ 1. *Whether this can be done or not* is no longer the question.

_____ 2. Most people believe the situation better *than it was in 1954.*

_____ 3. The unity *to which you contributed so indispensably* seems likely to be preserved.

_____ 4. He had yelled so often *that we could not believe him now.*

_____ 5. The diplomat saw clearly *that the enemy was trying to secure control of the conference.*

_____ 6. The President spoke *as if he were tired.*

_____ 7. *What the candidate planned to do* will now never be known.

_____ 8. The court ruled *that reporters must name their source of information.*

_____ 9. *Where there is no vision,* the people perish.

_____ 10. I talked to him *as an uncle.*

_____ 11. They give me *what I am looking for in comfort.*

_____ 12. They were led to a room *from which soon came the sound of songs and cheers.*

_____ 13. *"That won't be necessary,"* the patient's wife told the nurse.

_____ 14. For the thousands *whom he had taught* it was hard to visualize the school without him.

_____ 15. The Federal Trade Commission started a thorough study of *what caused recent mergers.*

_____ 16. The countryside is still sprinkled with hardy pioneers *who came West in covered wagons.*

_____ 17. This is *what I mean.*

_____ 18. They counted the bodies *as they were brought down the mountain.*

Exercises for

8. TYPES OF CLAUSES

Directions: In the blank write the number that identifies the type of dependent clause italicized in each sentence.

1. Adjective clause
2. Noun clause
3. Adverbial clause

_____ 1. Mr. and Mrs. Victor stayed downtown *in order that they might be near the shops and theaters.*

_____ 2. Few economists believe *that the United States can maintain "full employment."*

_____ 3. It was clear *that Sir Anthony must still wait.*

_____ 4. This was the place *where engineers had determined to locate the dam.*

_____ 5. I told him *where I had been.*

_____ 6. These are *what I wanted.*

_____ 7. The chair was so high *that she could not reach the floor with her toes.*

_____ 8. These people are the ones *whose money supported the revolution.*

_____ 9. *That we have at last reached an agreement* will come as a surprise to our enemies.

_____ 10. We determined *where the power lay.*

_____ 11. Popo, *as the Indians call the peak,* exacts its toll of climbers.

_____ 12. The child grabbed an apple *while there were still some in the dish.*

_____ 13. I know *you will rejoice with me in the good news.*

_____ 14. A donor *whose name has been withheld* gave twenty dollars.

_____ 15. The students argued about *who would present the petition.*

_____ 16. *Though the paper is not neat,* it is correct.

_____ 17. Be quiet *so that the baby will not awake.*

INDEX

175

ENGLISH
ESSENTIALS
With Self-Scoring Exercises

ANSWERS
TO THE EXERCISES

All exercises which were answered incorrectly should be re-studied. A thorough grasp of the fundamentals of grammar covered in these exercises should prove extremely helpful to students preparing for quizzes or examinations.

ANSWERS
TO THE EXERCISES

PAGE 5	PAGE 6	PAGE 7	PAGE 8	PAGE 9	PAGE 10
	_3_ 1.	_3_ 1.		_2_ 1.	_2_ 1.
		_2_ 2.	_1_ 1.		
_1_ 1.	_2_ 2.	_2_ 3.	_3_ 2.		_3_ 2.
_2_ 2.			_2_ 3.	_3_ 2.	_1_ 3.
_1_ 3.	_1_ 3.	_1_ 4.			_3_ 4.
_3_ 4.		_2_ 5.	_1_ 4.		
_1_ 5.	_2_ 4.	_1_ 6.		_1_ 3.	_1_ 5.
	_1_ 5.	_1_ 7.	_3_ 5.	_2_ 4.	_2_ 6.
_2_ 6.	_3_ 6.				
_2_ 7.		_2_ 8.	_3_ 6.	_2_ 5.	
_3_ 8.	_2_ 7.		_3_ 7.	_3_ 6.	_3_ 7.
_1_ 9.		_1_ 9.		_2_ 7.	_2_ 8.
_1_ 10.					_2_ 9.
_3_ 11.	_3_ 8.	_1_ 10.	_2_ 8.	_1_ 8.	
_2_ 12.		_3_ 11.	_3_ 9.	_2_ 9.	_2_ 10.
_1_ 13.	_2_ 9.	_2_ 12.	_2_ 10.		_3_ 11.

PAGE 11	PAGE 12	PAGE 13	PAGE 14	PAGE 19	PAGE 20
				_1_ 1.	_2_ 1.
				_1_ 2.	_1_ 2.
				_1_ 3.	_2_ 3.
					_1_ 4.
_2_ 1.	_1_ 1.	_1_ 1.		_2_ 4.	_2_ 5.
	_2_ 2.	_3_ 2.		_2_ 5.	_1_ 6.
_3_ 2.	_1_ 3.		_1_ 1.	_2_ 6.	_1_ 7.
	_2_ 4.	_2_ 3.	_2_ 2.		_1_ 8.
_2_ 3.	_3_ 5.	_3_ 4.	_3_ 3.	_1_ 7.	_1_ 9.
_3_ 4.	_3_ 6.	_1_ 5.		_1_ 8.	
_2_ 5.	_2_ 7.	_2_ 6.	_2_ 4.	_2_ 9.	_2_ 10.
	_3_ 8.		_3_ 5.	_1_ 10.	_1_ 11.
_1_ 6.	_1_ 9.	_1_ 7.	_3_ 6.		_1_ 12.
_3_ 7.	_2_ 10.	_3_ 8.	_2_ 7.	_2_ 11.	_2_ 13.
_1_ 8.				_1_ 12.	_2_ 14.
	_2_ 11.		_1_ 8.	_2_ 13.	_1_ 15.
_2_ 9.			_2_ 9.	_2_ 14.	_2_ 16.
	_1_ 12.	_1_ 9.	_3_ 10.	_1_ 15.	_1_ 17.
_2_ 10.	_2_ 13.	_3_ 10.		_1_ 16.	_1_ 18.
_2_ 11.	_2_ 14.			_1_ 17.	_1_ 19.

PAGE 21	PAGE 22	PAGE 23	PAGE 24	PAGE 27	PAGE 28
1 — 1.	1 — 1.	3 — 1.	2 — 1.	X — 1.	___ 1.
2 — 2.	2 — 2.	2 — 2.	2 — 2.	___ 2.	X — 2.
2 — 3.	1 — 3.	2 — 3.	1 — 3.	X — 3.	___ 3.
1 — 4.	2 — 4.	1 — 4.	2 — 4.	X — 4.	___ 4.
1 — 5.	1 — 5.	1 — 5.	1 — 5.	X — 5.	X — 5.
2 — 6.	1 — 6.	2 — 6.	1 — 6.	X — 6.	X — 6.
2 — 7.	1 — 7.	1 — 7.	2 — 7.	___ 7.	___ 7.
1 — 8.	1 — 8.	1 — 8.	2 — 8.	X — 8.	X — 8.
2 — 9.	2 — 9.	1 — 9.	1 — 9.	___ 9.	X — 9.
1 — 10.	2 — 10.	2 — 10.	2 — 10.	X — 10.	___ 10.
2 — 11.	1 — 11.	2 — 11.	1 — 11.	___ 11.	___ 11.
1 — 12.	1 — 12.	2 — 12.	1 — 12.	___ 12.	___ 12.
1 — 13.	1 — 13.	1 — 13.	2 — 13.	X — 13.	___ 13.
2 — 14.	1 — 14.	2 — 14.	1 — 14.	___ 14.	___ 14.
1 — 15.	2 — 15.	2 — 15.	1 — 15.	___ 15.	___ 15.
2 — 16.	2 — 16.	2 — 16.	2 — 16.	X — 16.	___ 16.
___ 17.	1 — 17.	1 — 17.	1 — 17.	X — 17.	___ 17.
1 — 18.	2 — 18.	1 — 18.	1 — 18.	___ 18.	___ 18.
		1 — 19.	1 — 19.	X — 19.	
		2 — 20.			

PAGE 29	PAGE 30	PAGE 33	PAGE 34	PAGE 35	PAGE 36

PAGE 29
1. —
2. X
3. X
4. —
5. X
6. —
7. X
8. —
9. —
10. X
11. —
12. —
13. —
14. X
15. X
16. —
17. —

PAGE 30
1. —
2. X
3. —
4. —
5. —
6. X
7. X
8. —
9. X
10. —
11. X
12. X
13. —
14. —
15. X
16. X
17. X

PAGE 33
1. 1
2. 1
3. 2
4. 1
5. 1
6. 2
7. 1
8. 1
9. 1
10. 1
11. 1
12. 2
13. 2
14. 2
15. 1
16. 1
17. 2
18. 1
19. 2
20. 2

PAGE 34
1. 1
2. 2
3. 1
4. 2
5. 2
6. 2
7. 1
8. 2
9. 2
10. 2
11. 1
12. 1
13. 1
14. 1
15. 1
16. 2
17. 2
18. 2
19. 2

PAGE 35
1. 1
2. 1
3. 2
4. 2
5. 2
6. 2
7. 2
8. 2
9. 2
10. 2
11. 2
12. 1
13. 1
14. 2
15. 1
16. 2
17. 2
18. 1
19. 1
20. 2

PAGE 36
1. 1
2. 2
3. 1
4. 1
5. 1
6. 1
7. 2
8. 2
9. 2
10. 2
11. 1
12. 2
13. 2
14. 1
15. 2
16. 2
17. 1
18. 2

PAGE 37	PAGE 38	PAGE 41	PAGE 42	PAGE 43	PAGE 44
1. _/_	1. _2_	1. X	1. X	1. ___	1. X
2. _2_	2. _/2_	2. ___	2. ___	2. X	2. ___
3. _/_	3.	3. X	3. ___	3. X	3. X
4. _2_	4. _2_	4. ___	4. X	4. ___	4. ___
5. _2_	5. _/_	5. ___	5. ___	5. X	5. X
6. _2_	6. _2_	6. X	6. X	6. X	6. ___
7. _/_	7. _2_	7. X	7. X	7. ___	7. ___
8. _2_	8. _/_	8. ___	8. ___	8. X	8. X
9. _/_	9. _2_	9. X	9. X	9. ___	9. X
10. _2_	10. _2_	10. ___	10. X	10. ___	10. X
11. _/_	11. _2_	11. X	11. X	11. X	11. ___
12. _/_	12. _/_	12. ___	12. ___	12. ___	12. X
13. _/_	13. _/_	13. ___	13. ___	13. X	13. X
14. _/_	14. _2_	14. ___	14. ___	14. ___	14. ___
15. _/_	15. _2_	15. X	15. X	15. X	15. ___
16. _2_	16. _/_	16. X	16. ___	16. ___	16. ___
17. _/_	17. _/_	17. ___	17. X	17. X	17. ___
18. _/_	18. _/_	18. X	18. ___	18. ___	18. X
19. _2_	19. _2_	19. X	19. X	19. ___	19. X
20. _2_	20. _2_	20. ___	20. X	20. ___	20. X
		21. X	21. X	21. ___	
		22. ___	22. X	22. X	
		23. ___	23. ___	23. ___	
		24. ___		24. X	
		25. X		25. ___	

PAGE 55	PAGE 56	PAGE 57
d f b 1.	b b d 1.	a e a e 1.
b d f 2.	b f b 2.	e b e a 2.
b d d 3.	f b b 3.	a a e e 3.
	f f b 4.	e d f e 4.
	a a e 5.	
a f f 4.		b a a a 5.
b f c 5.	f c c 6.	e a a f 6.
b e e 6.	a a f 7.	f b a a 7.
	d d b 8.	
b c c 7.		c e b a 8.
	a d d 9.	
f f a 8.	a e f 10.	f a a e 9.

PAGE 58	PAGE 59	PAGE 60
e f a e 1.	a a e e 1.	a a a b 1.
a a c e 2.	c e b a 2.	c d a c 2.
e e b e 3.		a c a c 3.
a d b a 4.	a a f e 3.	e f a f 4.
	d a e b 4.	
a a f a 5.		a a a a 5.
a a e e 6.	a e a f 5.	a a d a 6.
a a a a 7.		a e e e 7.
	e e e e 6.	e b a a 8.
a a b d 8.	b d c a 7.	c d a d 9.
a e e e 9.		

PAGE 61	PAGE 62	PAGE 63

PAGE 61

1. *eeea*
2. *ebee*
3. *dabd*
4. *aeea*
5. *aaac*
6. *ceaa*
7. *cead*
8. *aebe*

PAGE 62

1. *cead*
2. *ccbc*
3. *aacc*
4. *ccde*
5. *eecb*
6. *eeec*
7. *ceae*
8. *ecbe*
9. *cede*
10. *cbce*

PAGE 63

1. 1 ②3 4 5 6
2. ①2 3 4 5 6
3. 1 ②3 4 5 ⑥
4. 1 ②3 4 5 6
5. ①②③4 ⑤⑥
6. 1 2 ③4 5 6
7. ①②3 ④5 6
8. 1 2 3 4 5 6
9. 1 ②3 4 5 6
10. 1 ②③4 5 6
11. 1 ②3 4 5 6
12. 1 ②3 ④5 6
13. 1 2 ③4 5 6
14. 1 ②③4 5 6
15. 1 ②3 ④5 ⑥

PAGE 64	PAGE 71	PAGE 72	PAGE 73	PAGE 74
		1. 3	1. 3	1. ___
	1. 2	2. 2	2. 1	
1 ②3 4 5 6 1.	2. 4	3. ___	3. 3	2. 4
		4. 4		
	3. ___	5. 3	4. ___	3. 3
1 ②3 4 5 6 2.	4. 3			
	5. 3		5. ___	4. 2
①2 ③4 5 6 3.	6. 4	6. 1	6. 1	5. 3
		7. ___	7. 4	6. 1
1 2 3 ④⑤6 4.	7. ___		8. 2	
	8. 1	8. 3	9. 3	7. ___
1 ②3 4 5 6 5.	9. 2	9. ___		
	10. 3	10. 4	10. 1	8. 4
①②③4 5 6 6.	11. 1	11. 1	11. 3	9. 2
	12. 4	12. ___	12. 4	
	13. ___	13. 2	13. ___	10. 1
1 ②3 4 5 6 7.	14. 4	14. 4	14. 3	11. 2
		15. 3	15. 4	12. 4
①②3 4 5 ⑥ 8.	15. 3	16. 3	16. 4	13. 4
1 ②3 ④5 6 9.	16. 2	17. ___	17. ___	14. 1
		18. ___	18. 3	15. 3
1 2 3 4 5 6 10.	17. ___	19. ___	19. ___	16. ___
				17. 2
①2 ③④5 ⑥ 11.	18. ___	20. 1	20. 1	18. 4
	19. 2	21. 2	21. 4	19. ___
1 ②3 4 5 6 12.		22. ___		20. 3
	20. ___	23. 1	22. 2	21. 1
1 2 3 ④5 ⑥ 13.	21. ___	24. ___	23. 2	22. ___
1 ②3 ④⑤6 14.	22. 4		24. 3	23. 2
	23. 3	25. 2	25. 4	
	24. 4			24. 1
1 2 3 4 5 ⑥ 15.	25. 1			25. 4

PAGE 75		PAGE 76		PAGE 81		PAGE 82		PAGE 87		PAGE 88	
1	1.	4	1.	2	1.	1	1.				1.
	2.	4	2.	1	2.	2	2.	4	1.	2	2.
4	3.	1	3.	2	3.	2	3.	1	2.	4	3.
2	4.		4.	2	4.	2	4.	4	3.		4.
1	5.	4	5.	1	5.	1	5.		4.	1	5.
	6.	2	6.	2	6.	2	6.			3	6.
3	7.					2	7.	3	5.		7.
1	8.	2	7.	2	7.	2	8.	1	6.		
4	9.		8.	1	8.	2	9.		7.	1	8.
	10.	1	9.	2	9.	2	10.	3	8.		9.
	11.	3	10.	2	10.	2	11.	2	9.		
3	12.	1	11.	3	11.	1	12.	3	10.		
3	13.	2	12.	1	12.	1	13.	1	11.	2	10.
1	14.	(1)	13.	2	13.	1	14.				
4	15.	3	14.	2	14.	2	15.	4	12.	1	11.
3	16.	4	15.	1	15.	2	16.		13.	2	12.
2	17.	4	16.	2	16.	2	17.	2	14.		
1	18.	1	17.	3	17.	1	18.				13.
4	19.	2	18.	1	18.	1	19.	1	15.	4	14.
4	20.		19.	2	19.						
3	21.	3	20.								
3	22.	3	21.								
2	23.	1	22.								
1	24.		23.								
4	25.	2	24.								
		1	25.								

PAGE 89	PAGE 91	PAGE 92	PAGE 93	PAGE 94
		_2_ 9.		1 2 3 ④⑤ 5.
		_3_ 10.		
		_2_ 11.		
		_3_ 12.		
		_3_ 13.		1 2 3 4 ⑤ 6.
_3_ 1.				
_2_ 2.				
_1_ 3.				
_3_ 4.			①②3 4 ⑤ 1.	①2③④5 7.
___ 5.				
_4_ 6.	_2_ 1.			
_1_ 7.	_1_ 2.			①②3④⑤ 8.
_4_ 8.				
_3_ 9.	_3_ 3.		1 2 3 4 ⑤ 2.	
___ 10.	_1_ 4.			
_3_ 11.	_2_ 5.			①②3 4 ⑤ 9.
_1_ 12.			①2③4 5 3.	
_2_ 13.	_3_ 6.			
_4_ 14.				
___ 15.	_1_ 7.		1 2 3 4 ⑤ 4.	1 2 ③4 5 10.
_1_ 16.	_1_ 8.			
_2_ 17.				

PAGE 95	PAGE 96	PAGE 97

1 2 3 ④ 5   11.

① 2 ③ ④ 5   12.

① ② ③ ④ 5   13.

1 ② ③ ④ ⑤   14.

1 ② 3 4 ⑤   15.

1 ② 3 ④ ⑤   16.

① 2 ③ 4 ⑤   17.

1 ② ③ ④ ⑤   18.

gefe   1.

aaae   2.

aaee   3.

eeaa   4.

aaad   5.

bdac   6.

dabe   7.

eead   8.

ffeb   9.

PAGE 98	PAGE 99	PAGE 100	PAGE 101	PAGE 102
		3 13.		
				①2③4⑤ 7.
		2 14.		
1 1.		3 15.		
___ 2.				①2③4⑤ 8.
___ 3.			1②345 1.	
___ 4.				①2③4⑤ 8.
4 5.				
1 6.				
4 7.			①②③④5 2.	
3 8.				1 2 3④5 9.
4 9.				
3 10.	3 1.			
1 11.	1 2.		1②③4⑤ 3.	
2 12.				1 2 3 4⑤ 10.
4 13.	2 3.			
3 14.	3 4.			
___ 15.				
4 16.	2 5.		①2 3④⑤ 4.	1②3④5 11.
___ 17.	1 6.			
2 18.	3 7.			
3 19.			1②③④⑤ 5.	
___ 20.	1 8.			1 2③④⑤ 12.
3 21.	2 9.			
___ 22.	3 10.			
4 23.				
___ 24.	1 11.		①2 3 4⑤ 6.	1 2 3④⑤ 13.
2 25.	2 12.			

PAGE 103	PAGE 104	PAGE 105	PAGE 107

PAGE 103

1 2 3 4 5 14.

1 ②③④⑤ 15.

①②③ 4 5 16.

①②3 ④⑤ 17.

1 ②3 4⑤ 18.

PAGE 104

a a f e 1.

f b d g 2.

a c a d 3.

a g a f 4.

a d d d 5.

a a b a 6.

a e a b 7.

e f a d 8.

PAGE 105

4 1.
2 2.
___ 3.
2 4.
4 5.
1 6.
2 7.
1 8.
___ 9.
3 19.
4 11.
3 12.
___ 13.
2 14.
4 15.
1 16.
___ 17.
___ 18.
4 19.
3 20.
3 21.
1 22.
2 23.
1 24.
4 25.

PAGE 107

1 1.
3 2.
2 3.
1 4.
2 5.
2 6.
2 7.
2 8.

PAGE 108	PAGE 109	PAGE 110	PAGE 111
2 9.		(1)(2)3(4)5 7.	1 2(3)(4)(5) 14.
2 10.			
1 11.			
3 12.	(1)(2)3(4)5 1.	(1)(2)3 4(5) 8.	(1)2 3(4)(5) 15.
1 13.			
	1(2)(3)(4)(5) 2.	(1)(2)3 4(5) 9.	(1)(2)(3)4 5 16.
	1(2)3(4)5 3.	1(2)(3)4(5) 10.	1(2)(3)4(5) 17.
		1 2 3(4)5 11.	
	(1)2 3 4(5) 4.		(1)(2)3(4)(5) 18.
		(1)2(3)(4)5 12.	
	1(2)(3)(4)(5) 5.		
		(1)(2)3 4(5) 13.	
	1 2(3)(4)5 6.		

ANSWERS TO SELF-SCORING EXERCISES

PAGE 112	PAGE 113	PAGE 117	PAGE 118	PAGE 119
	___ 1.	3 1.	2 1.	1 ___ ___ ___ 1.
	1 2.	6 2.	2 2.	2 ___ ___ ___ 2.
	3 3.	___ 3.	2 3.	2 3 ___ ___ 3.
facc 1.	2 4.	1 4.	3 4.	2 3 5 ___ 4.
	4 5.	7 5.	___ 5.	2 3 4 5 5.
fead 2.	___ 6.	6 6.	2 6.	2 6 ___ ___ 6.
	1 7.	2 7.	1 7.	2 4 5 ___ 7.
cdac 3.	1 8.	5 8.	3 8.	1 3 ___ ___ 8.
	___ 9.	2 9.	4 9.	2 3 ___ ___ 9.
aaaf 4.	4 10.	12 10.	3 10.	2 4 ___ ___ 10.
	2 11.	___ 11.	5 11.	1 ___ ___ ___ 11.
	3 12.	1 12.	1 12.	1 ___ ___ ___ 12.
baea 5.	1 13.	5 13.	6 13.	2 3 4 ___ 13.
	3 14.	5 14.	3 14.	3 5 7 ___ 14.
aaee 6.	___ 15.	2 15.	5 15.	2 ___ ___ ___ 15.
	2 16.	___ 16.	4 16.	1 4 ___ ___ 16.
faba 7.	___ 17.	___ 17.	8 17.	2 ___ ___ ___ 17.
	3 18.	6 18.	1 18.	2 3 4 ___ 18.
aaba 8.	1 19.	4 19.	8 19.	2 4 5 6 19.
	4 20.	1 20.	___ 20.	1 3 ___ ___ 20.
	___ 21.			
	1 22.			
eeaa 9.	___ 23.			
	4 24.			
	___ 25.			

PAGE 120	PAGE 121

PAGE 120

3 4 _ _ 1.
3 _ _ _ 2.
2 3 4 _ 3.
2 _ _ _ 4.
3 4 5 6 5.
2 3 _ _ 6.
2 _ _ _ 7.
2 4 _ _ 8.
3 4 5 _ 9.
2 _ _ _ 10.
2 3 4 5 11.

2 _ _ _ 12.
3 _ _ _ 13.
2 4 _ _ 14.
1 _ _ _ 15.
3 4 5 6 16.

4 5 _ _ 17.
5 _ _ _ 18.

3 5 6 7 19.

3 5 6 _ 20.

PAGE 121

1   2 3 4 _ 1.

8   5 _ _ _ 2.

7   2 4 _ _ 3.

1   2 4 5 _ 4.

1   4 _ _ _ 5.
2   3 4 5 _ 6.

3   2 4 _ _ 7.

2   3 _ _ _ 8.
1   5 6 _ _ 9.

2   3 6 7 8 10.

1   2 3 _ _ 11.
3   2 4 _ _ 12.
7   2 3 4 _ 13.

4   2 _ _ _ 14.
2   3 6 _ _ 15.

1   2 _ _ _ 16.

PAGE 122	PAGE 123

PAGE 122

_3_ _4 6_ __ __ 1.

_1_ _2 3 4 5_ 2.

_3_ _2 4_ __ __ 3.

_7_ _2 3 4_ __ 4.

_4_ _5 7 8 9_ 5.

_2_ _6_ __ __ __ 6.

_1_ _5 6 7_ __ 7.

_1_ _5 6 7 8_ 8.

_1_ _5 6_ __ __ 9.

_7_ _4_ __ __ 10.

_2_ _3 4 5_ __ 11.

_2_ _1 3_ __ __ 12.

_1_ _4 5 6_ __ 13.

_2_ _3 4 5 6_ 14.

PAGE 123

_5_ _6 7 9_ __ 1.

_3_ _4_ __ __ __ 2.
_1_ _4 5_ __ __ 3.

_1_ _3_ __ __ __ 4.

_5_ _6_ __ __ __ 5.

_2_ _1 4 5_ __ 6.

_3_ _4 6_ __ __ 7.

_1_ _2_ __ __ __ 8.

_2_ _3 4 5 6_ 9.

_4_ _1 2_ __ __ 10.

_1_ _2_ __ __ 11.
_3_ _4 5_ __ __ 12.

_1_ _4 5_ __ __ 13.

_2_ _1 3 4_ __ 14.

_8_ _9 10 11 12_ 15.

_3_ _4_ __ __ __ 16.

_7_ _4_ __ __ __ 17.

_1_ _2 3 4_ __ 18.

	PAGE 124	PAGE 127	PAGE 128	PAGE 129
1.	4 56	2	2	1
2.	3 4567	1	1	2
3.	3 467	2	2	1
4.	7 5	1	1	1
5.	1 23	2	1	1
6.	2 357	1	2	1
7.	1 234	2	2	1
8.	7 4	1	2	1
9.	3 1	2	1	1
10.	2 578	1	1	2
11.	2 3	1	1	2
12.	1 46	2	2	1
13.	1 2	1	1	1
14.	1 24	2	2	2
15.	2 13	1	1	2
16.	4 35	2	2	1
17.	1 2345	2	1	2
18.	2 46	1	2	2
19.		2	1	2
20.		2	2	2
21.		1	1	1
22.		1	2	1

PAGE 130	PAGE 131	PAGE 132	PAGE 137	PAGE 138
1. 1	1. 1	1. 1	1. 37	
2. 2	2. 2	2. 2	2. 48	1. 68
3. 1	3. 1	3. 2	3. 67	2. 57
4. 1	4. 2	4. 1	4. 45	3. 17 18
5. 2	5. 2	5. 2	5. 12	4. 57
6. 1	6. 1	6. 2	6. 46	5. 78
7. 2	7. 2	7. 2	7. 25	6. 9 11
8. 2	8. 2	8. 1	8. 56	7. 46
9. 1	9. 2	9. 2	9. 14	8. 89
10. 2	10. 2	10. 1	10. 57	9. 57
11. 1	11. 1	11. 2	11. 68	10. 14
12. 2	12. 1	12. 2	12. 13	11. 68
13. 1	13. 1	13. 1	13. 69	12. 45
14. 1	14. 2	14. 1	14. 67	13. 59
15. 2	15. 1	15. 2	15. 14	14. 13
16. 1	16. 1	16. 2		15. 56
17. 2	17. 2	17. 2		
18. 2	18. 2	18. 1		
19. 1	19. 2	19. 1		
20. 2	20. 2	20. 1		
21. 2	21. 1	21. 2		
22. 1	22. 1	22. 1		

PAGE 139	PAGE 140	PAGE 145	PAGE 146	PAGE 147	PAGE 148
7 8 1.					
5 6 2.	6 9 1.				
4 6 3.	7 9 2.				2 1.
5 9 4.	4 5 3.	1 1.	4 1.	4 1.	1 2.
	6 8 4.	1 2.	1 2.	1 2.	2 3.
4 6 5.		2 3.	2 3.	1 3.	4 4.
9 11 6.	7 8 5.	3 4.	3 4.	3 4.	3 5.
		3 5.	1 5.	4 5.	2 6.
5 6 7.	2 3 6.	2 6.	4 6.	2 6.	1 7.
6 9 8.	6 9 7.	1 7.	3 7.	1 7.	4 8.
	1 4 8.		1 8.	2 8.	2 9.
5 6 9.		1 8.	2 9.	4 9.	4 10.
7 11 10.	3 5 9.	3 9.	1 10.	4 10.	1 11.
		2 10.	2 11.	1 11.	
10 14 11.	9 10 10.	4 11.	4 12.	4 12.	1 12.
		1 12.	4 13.	2 13.	4 13.
1 2 12.	4 6 11.	1 13.	1 14.	2 14.	3 14.
3 7 13.	2 3 12.	2 14.	1 15.	1 15.	4 15.
	7 10 13.	2 15.	1 16.	4 16.	2 16.
5 8 14.	7 10 14.	3 16.	3 17.	2 17.	2 17.
5 10 15.		4 17.			
	5 6 15.	2 18.	4 18.	4 18.	4 18.

PAGE 155	PAGE 156	PAGE 157	PAGE 158	PAGE 167	PAGE 168
1. 1	1. 2	1. 3	1. 3	1. 1 4	1. 3 6
2. 2	2. 1	2. 1	2. 1	2. 3 6	2. 6 12
3. 3	3. 1	3. 2	3. 1	3. 1 5	3. 1 4
4. 1	4. 2	4. 2	4. 2	4. 4 8	4. 1 8
5. 2	5. 3	5. 1	5. 3	5. 8 11	5. 1 3
6. 1	6. 1	6. 3	6. 1	6. 1 4	6. 6 13
7. 2	7. 2	7. 2	7. 2	7. 7 10	7. 6 10
8. 1	8. 1	8. 1	8. 3	8. 2 5	8. 1 3
9. 3	9. 3	9. 1	9. 2	9. 8 13	9. 6 11
10. 1	10. 1	10. 1	10. 1	10. 6 9	10. 7 13
11. 3	11. 1	11. 2	11. 3	11. 1 4	11. 5 11
12. 2	12. 3	12. 3	12. 2	12. 4 10	12. 5 8
13. 1	13. 1	13. 1	13. 2	13. 7 10	13. 5 9
14. 1	14. 2	14. 1	14. 3	14. 2 7	14. 1 4
15. 1	15. 3	15. 1	15. 2	15. 6 7	15. 5 11
16. 3	16. 3	16. 2	16. 3		16. 11 15
17. 1	17. 2	17. 1	17. 1		17. 5 16
18. 2	18. 2	18. 3	18. 3		
19. 2	19. 2	19. 2			

PAGE 169	PAGE 170	PAGE 171	PAGE 172	PAGE 173
1. 9 13	1. 9 14			
2. 4 8	2. 3 9	1. 3	1. 3	1. 2
3. 1 8	3. 1 8	2. 1	2. 2	2. 3
4. 7 10	4. 5 10	3. 2	3. 2	3. 1
5. 1 8	5. 4 5	4. 1	4. 1	4. 3
6. 10 17	6. 5 11	5. 3	5. 1	5. 2
7. 1 4	7. 5 6	6. 3	6. 3	6. 3
8. 5 11	8. 6 16	7. 2	7. 3	7. 2
9. 3 4	9. 4 10	8. 2	8. 1	8. 2
10. 5 6	10. 4 11	9. 1	9. 2	9. 3
11. 6 8	11. 1 5	10. 3	10. 3	10. 3
12. 6 12	12. 4 7	11. 1	11. 1	11. 2
13. 7 16	13. 4 10	12. 2	12. 2	12. 1
14. 6 11	14. 3 8	13. 3	13. 3	13. 2
15. 8 15	15. 8 12	14. 1	14. 3	14. 1
		15. 2	15. 2	15. 2
				16. 1
				17. 2
				18. 3

PAGE 174

_3_ 1.

_2_ 2.

_2_ 3.

_1_ 4.

_2_ 5.

_2_ 6.

_3_ 7.

_1_ 8.

_2_ 9.

_ 10.

11.

_3_ 12.

_2_ 13.

_1_ 14.

_2_ 15.

_3_ 16.

_3_ 17.